Discover other titles by Breathair Publishing

Prof. Arnold Ehret's Mucusless Diet Healing System: Annotated, Revised, and Edited by Prof. Spira

Spira Speaks: Dialogs and Essays on the Mucusless Diet Healing System

Prof. Arnold Ehret's Rational Fasting for Physical, Mental and Spiritual Rejuvenation: Introduced and Edited by Prof. Spira

Thus Speaketh the Stomach and the Tragedy of Nutrition: Introduced and Edited by Prof. Spira

The Definite Cure of Chronic Constipation and Overcoming Constipation Naturally: Introduced and Edited by Prof. Spira

Physical Fitness Thru a Superior Diet, Fasting, and Dietetics Also a Religious Concept of Physical, Spiritual, and Mental Dietetics: Introduced & Edited by Prof. Spira

Coming Soon

Art of Transition: Spira's Mucusless Diet Healing System Menu and Recipe Guide

CONTENTS

A Note to the Reader

THESE NOTES ARE NOT INTENDED AND HAVE NOT BEEN PREPARED TO SERVE AS A SUBSTITUTE FOR *PROF. ARNOLD EHRET'S MUCUSLESS DIET HEALING SYSTEM,* LECTURES BASED ON THE CONTENT OF THE BOOK, OR FOR CLASSROOM DISCUSSION AND ANALYSIS OF THE TEXT.

This edition of *Spira's Notes* is specifically designed to accompany Prof. Spira's *Mucusless Diet Healing System eCourse: Keys for Mastering a Mucus-free Life.* Although it is primarily based on Spira's annotated, revised, and edited edition of *Prof. Arnold Ehret's Mucusless Diet Healing System,* it may act as an apt companion to any edition of the original work.

Inspired by the famous *CliffsNotes* series of study guides, the aim is to summarize, outline, analyze, and provide review materials that cover the most important points of the *Mucusless Diet Healing System* text.

How to Use this Study Guide

"This book represents an outline of the serious nature of my work and it also appeals to you for help in carrying it through as the greatest deed you can perform—upon which depends not only your future destiny, but that of a suffering, unhappy humankind—on the verge of physical and mental collapse." – Arnold Ehret in the Mucusless Diet Healing System

Greetings Brothers and Sisters!

Part of my life's mission is to help carry Arnold Ehret's message forth to people of the 21st century, many of whom are in desperate need of his wisdom. In the early 1900s, Ehret found answers to some of humanity's most difficult questions, and for over 100 years, too few people have had the privilege of hearing his message. The intention of this study guide is to play a major role in changing this! Billions of people around the world can and will benefit from Ehret's message, but the necessary educational tools must be developed and made available for health seekers and health educators alike.

This edition of *Spira's Notes: The Official Mucusless Diet Healing System eCourse Study Guide* is first and foremost a companion to *Prof. Arnold Ehret's Mucusless Diet Healing System: Annotated, Revised, and Edited by Prof. Spira*. This guide is not meant to replace reading or listening to the audiobook of the original *Mucusless Diet* text. The intention is to facilitate further study for students of my *Mucusless Diet Healing System eCourse*, as well as students of Arnold Ehret's work in general.

Many students of the eCourse will not only gain the tools to become lifelong practitioners of the diet, but also health educators inspired to share Ehret's message with their families, friends, patients, and students. Each lesson from the *Mucusless Diet* book is broken down into several corresponding components in this guide, including lesson summaries, outlines, glossaries, review questions, and in some cases, a list of books to consider for further reading.

Students of the eCourse are asked to first read and listen to the full text of each lesson from the *Annotated, Revised, and Edited Mucusless Diet*, then watch my short video discussions of the lesson, and then finally use this book to review the main points from the aforementioned. If you follow this simple formula, you will develop a firm grasp of Ehret's methods and be empowered to move forward with your healing journey confidently.

For educators, this book provides resources that will allow you to share Ehret's message more efficiently. The layout and formatting of the text make it the perfect companion for leading informal round-table discussions, giving lectures, preparing your own lecture notes, and designing seminars. Each lesson starts with the summary on odd-numbered pages, followed by the outline on the following even-numbered pages. In most cases, the entire outline fits on two or three pages. This will help discussion leaders and lecturers use the outline as a guide without the need to constantly turn pages or skim through the full *Mucusless Diet* text for main points during their presentations.

The glossary sections include key words from each lesson with brief definitions or discussions. A number of the definitions are composed and adapted by me based upon Arnold Ehret's original concepts or material. Some keywords and their definitions derive from relevant idiomatic phrases developed and used within the mucus-free community. Others are standard definitions in which I surveyed multiple sources and construct definitions that best matches the context and meaning of Ehret's usage of the term. Sources in which I consulted include Merriam-Webster.com, Etymonline.com, Britannica.com, OxfordDictionaries.com, MedicineNet.com, BusinessDictionary.com, OxfordReference.com, Dictionary.com, Wiktionary.org, Wikipedia.com, and CollinsDictionary.com.

A number of ancient wisdom traditions teach that we humans feel our best and are most at peace with the Universe when we RECEIVE FOR THE SAKE OF SHARING. When we obtain knowledge, love, resources, strength, wisdom, freedom, etc., it is a Universal law that we feel our best when we can share some bit of it with others in ways that enhance their lives. My hope is that this study guide enables you to effortlessly receive and understand Ehret's message with such proficiency that you are not only able to transform your own health for the better, but feel so wonderful that you are compelled to share this information with others. Share freely and without judgment, as you never know who will discover Ehret's work, "get it," and begin their own journey back to the paradisiacal lifestyle that Arnold Ehret envisioned for humanity.

Peace, Love, and Breath!

-Prof. Spira, PhD, July 2017

Prof. Arnold Ehret's Biography

Summary: Arnold Ehret's Biography

Professor Arnold Ehret was a German healer, dietitian, philosopher, teacher, and visionary, one of the first people to advocate fasting and a plant-based, vegan, and mucus-free lifestyle as a therapy for healing. At the age of 31, he was diagnosed with Bright's disease (inflammation of the kidneys) and pronounced incurable by doctors. After seeking help from medical and drugless healers, he learned the power of fasting when he lost hope and stopped eating. Within two weeks he felt better, healed himself, and started a journey that led him to discover the principles of healing that he used to save thousands of so-called "incurable" patients in his sanitariums, and ultimately through his written works. For over 100 years, his books and teachings have touched the lives of thousands of health-seekers pursuing higher levels of vitality. Ehret's most famous books, *Mucusless Diet Healing System* and *Rational Fasting*, continue to increase in popularity as plant-based, vegan, and raw-food diets become more prevalent. Ehret believed that pus- and mucus-forming foods were unnatural for humans to eat and suggested that a diet of fruits and green-leaf vegetables (i.e., mucus-free foods), are the most healing and powerful foods for humans. Ehret offers a sophisticated yet simple and safe transitional system for those who endeavor to stop eating pus- and mucus-forming foods.

Outline: Arnold Ehret's Biography

1) Introduction

   a) Arnold Ehret was a German healer, dietitian, philosopher, teacher, visionary, and fasting expert.

      i) He was one of the first to advocate plant-based, vegan, and mucus-free healing methods.

   b) For over 100 years, his teachings have touched the lives of thousands of health seekers.

   c) His most famous books:

      i) *Mucusless Diet Healing System* and *Rational Fasting.*

2) Early Life

   a) Ehret was born on July 25, 1866.

      i) There is a discrepancy regarding the date of his birth, and some of his biographical texts say July 29, 1866.

   b) Ehret loved studying.

      i) Interested in physics, chemistry, drawing, painting, and linguistics.

         (1) He could speak German, French, Italian, and English.

      ii) At age 21, he graduated as a professor of drawing.

         (1) He was drafted into the military, but was discharged due to heart trouble.

   c) At age 31, he was diagnosed with Bright's disease (inflammation of the kidneys).

      i) This caused him to investigate natural healing.

      ii) After only having some success, he lost hope and stopped eating.

         (1) He started to heal and realized the power of fasting.

   d) In 1899, he traveled to Berlin to study vegetarianism.

      i) He then took a trip to Algiers in northern Africa where he experimented with fasting, fruit dieting, and vitalism.

   e) Because of his newfound lifestyle, he overcame all of his ailments.

3) Successful Healer

   a) In the early 1900s, Ehret opened a sanitarium in Ascona, Switzerland, where he treated and healed thousands of patients.

      i) Many patients were considered "incurable."

   b) Fasting World Record

      i) Within 14 months, Ehret completed a series of fasts, ending with a 49-day fast monitored by Swiss officials.

   c) In 1914, Ehret traveled to the U.S. to see the Panama Exposition and sample the fruits of the continent.

i) He was unable to return to Germany due to World War I and settled in Mount Washington near Los Angeles, California.

    (1) He prepared his written manuscripts and opened a sanitarium in Alhambra, California.

ii) He developed a course of which the *Mucusless Diet Healing System* became the textbook.

4) Death

  a) On October 9, 1922, he finished a series of lectures on the "Grape Cure."

    i) His final lecture was at the Assembly Room of the Angeles Hotel to a sold-out crowd.

    ii) After leaving the building, Ehret allegedly fell and sustained a fatal blow to his skull.

      (1) No one saw his death.

      (2) Fred Hirsch, Ehret's business partner and confidant, claims that he found Ehret after he fell.

    iii) There is much speculation about Ehret's death.

      (1) The story does not add up for many of Ehret's followers, who believe that foul play may have been involved.

5) Legacy

  a) Arnold Ehret is a cultural icon and protagonist of the emerging back-to-nature renaissance.

  b) Throughout the 20th century, Ehret's teachings have thrived and developed through the efforts of dedicated followers.

  c) Today his teachings are gaining wider acceptance throughout the world as people seek to investigate plant-based, vegan healing, and detoxification.

Glossary: Arnold Ehret's Biography

Bright's Disease: A historical categorization of kidney diseases that would be characterized as acute or chronic nephritis in contemporary medical terminology.

Fred Hirsch (1888–1979): After his diagnosis of necrosis of the Achilles caused by a bone infection in both heels, Hirsch attended a lecture of Arnold Ehret's in California. Hirsch, who knew some German, helped Ehret with English words he was having trouble with. Following the lecture, the two spoke, and Ehret befriended him, vowing to help him heal. After an extended fast monitored by Ehret, Hirsch healed and was no longer in need of crutches. Hirsch soon became Ehret's business manager. When Ehret diet in 1922, Hirsch continued to run the Ehret Publishing Company and the Ehret Health Club, published the club's newsletter, and ran a popular health retreat named Highland Springs Resort.

Back-to-Nature Renaissance (Back-to-Nature Movement): A social, countercultural movement that began in the late 1800s, originally led by German youth. In the wake of the European industrial revolution, young activists rejected urbanization and middle-class social norms. Inspired by works of

Nietzsche, Goethe, Hesse, and also by pagan religions, thousands of German youth endeavored to return to a more natural way of life in tune with natural laws. This movement caused great advancements in the area of natural healing, as many began to research and experiment with fasting cures and plant-based fruit and vegetable diets as a sustainable way to live. During the early part of the twentieth century, many Germans moved to the United States and settled in southern California. Natural healers and back-to-nature advocates such as Arnold Ehret had a profound influence on American youth and spurred on the countercultural revolution in the United States, as well as the cultivation of naturopathy, the natural-hygienic movement, and the 1960s hippie culture (See Gordon Kennedy's *Children of Sun*).

Benedict Lust (1872–1945): German-born pioneer of naturopathy who organized the first naturopathic medical school in the world as well as the first professional organization of naturopathic physicians called the American Naturopathic Association. Lust was influenced by Ehret's work and became his first publisher in the United States. Benedict Lust Publications continues to publish editions of Ehret's works.

Review Questions: Arnold Ehret's Biography

1. What is the name of the so-called incurable disease that Arnold Ehret suffered from?

2. What prevented Ehret from traveling back to Europe when he visited the U.S. in 1914?

3. Arnold Ehret was a leader in what some historians call the "Back-to-Nature Renaissance." (True or False)

4. Today, an increased number of people are learning about Ehret's teachings and adopting plant-based, mucus-free lifestyles. (True or False)

Further Reading: Arnold Ehret's Biography

Child, B. W. Circa 1922. "Biographical Sketch of Prof. Arnold Ehret." In *Prof. Arnold Ehret's Physical Fitness Thru a Superior Diet, Fasting, and Dietetics*. 2017. Columbus, OH: Breathair Publishing.

Kennedy, Gordon. 1998. "Arnold Ehret." In *Children of the Sun: A Pictorial Anthology, from Germany to California*, 1883–1949, 144–153. Ojai, CA: Nivaria Press.

Lesson I
General Introductory Principles

Summary: Lesson I

In Lesson I, Prof. Arnold Ehret offers a general introduction to his Mucusless Diet Healing System. First, he defines "constipation" as the foundation of human illness and explains that it comes from uneliminated, unnatural food substances accumulated since childhood. Second, he proclaims that his Mucusless Diet Healing System is the answer to healing human illness and that many "declared-incurable patients" could be saved through its practice. Third, Ehret defines the mucusless diet as a diet consisting of all kinds of raw and cooked fruits, starchless vegetables, and raw and cooked green-leaf vegetables. The Mucusless Diet as a Healing System, however, is described as an eloquent system that employs progressively changing menus that move from a mucus-heavy diet toward a mucus-free diet, as well as individually advised forms of fasting in alignment with the needs of each practitioner. Finally, Ehret identifies the human body as an elastic pipe system and observes that the average person's diet is never fully eliminated, which results in toxic residues accumulating in the body. These toxic residues ultimately become the foundation of human illness. Ehret asserts that his healing system is the only way to remove the waste intelligently and carefully, thereby establishing the internal environment in which the body heals itself.

Outline: Lesson I

1) What Is Constipation?
   a) Every disease, despite the name by which it is known, is "CONSTIPATION."
      i) Ehret defines "constipation" as a clogging up of the entire pipe system of the human body.
      ii) Symptoms of disease occur from accumulated mucus in a specific location in the body.
   b) Accumulation points include:
      i) Tongue, stomach, and entire digestive tract.
      ii) The average person may have as much as 10 pounds of uneliminated feces in the bowels poisoning the bloodstream.
      iii) Every sick person is clogged with mucus and waste.
   c) Where does the mucus come from?
      i) "Undigested, uneliminated, and unnatural food substances accumulated since childhood."
   d) Ehret's "Mucus-Theory" and *Mucusless Diet Healing System*
      i) Proven to be the most successful "compensation action" or therapy of eating to overcome human illness.
         (1) Ehret asserts, "Thousands of declared-incurable patients could be saved" using the methods found in the *Mucusless Diet*.
   e) What is the Mucusless Diet?
      i) (Strict definition) All kinds of raw and cooked fruits, starchless vegetables, and cooked or raw, mostly green-leaf vegetables.
   f) What is the Mucusless Diet as a *Healing System*?
      i) It is a systematic combination of progressively changing menus toward mucus-free foods, or what Ehret calls the "transition diet" in later lessons, individually advised short- or long-term fasting, as well as ancillary therapies such as enemas, exercise, and sunbathing.

2) What Is Vitality?
   a) Ehret affirms that the human body and the cause of human illness are still a mystery to medical scientists.
   b) Simplicity is key!
      i) Ehret says, "*whatever simple reason* cannot be grasped is *humbug*, however *scientific* it may sound."
   c) You will learn:
      i) How wrong it is to think that disease can be healed by just eating the "right foods" or special menus.
      ii) The complete "system" must be understood and applied for success.
      iii) Each person's situation is different, and special advice must be considered for each individual case.

3) What Is Fasting?

a) Abstaining from food and/or drink for an indefinite period of time.

b) Ehret asserts that fasting has been used for millennia to naturally heal sick people.

    i) Fasting and Mucusless Diet are "Nature's only and infallible laws."

      (1) Stated in the biblical book of Genesis as "fruits and herbs," i.e., green leaves.

c) Why do some fasting attempts fail?

    i) Because they are not used systematically according to the condition of the patient.

4) What Is Disease?

a) Ehret says "Disease is an effort of the body to eliminate waste, mucus, and toxemias."

b) "Not the disease, but the body is to be healed."

    i) To do this, the body must be cleansed of accumulated foreign matter and toxic waste.

c) The Healing System is not a cure, but a regeneration of the human body, mind, and spirit.

d) All disease has its primary source in a filthy colon.

e) "What medical science calls 'normal health' is in fact a pathological condition."

    i) In other words, what is considered normal and "healthy" is actually a sick/diseased condition.

5) In Summa

a) The human body is an elastic pipe system.

b) The diet of civilization is not properly digested or its waste eliminated.

c) The pipe system becomes slowly constipated.

d) This constipation directly or indirectly causes all human illnesses.

e) To loosen and eliminate this waste properly can only be done by the Mucusless Diet Healing System.

Glossary: Lesson I

Constipation: Ehret defines "constipation" as "a clogging up of the entire pipe system of the human body" with waste. The term may also be used to refer to an acute or chronic condition in which there is difficulty emptying the bowels because of an accumulation of hard, dry, and/or sticky fecal matter. Ehret is referring to constipation throughout the entire organism and not just the bowels.

Mucus: The word "mucus" is from the Latin *mucus* meaning "slime, mold, snot, etc." Mucus refers to a thick, viscous, slippery discharge that is comprised of dead cells, mucin, inorganic salts, water, and exfoliated cells. It also refers to the slimy, sticky, viscous substance left behind by mucus-forming foods in the body after ingestion.

Mucus Theory: A philosophical and theoretical framework created by Prof. Arnold Ehret that identifies mucus-forming foods as unnatural and indigestible for the human body. It is asserted that these foods leave behind uneliminated waste in the body which is the primary cause of human illness and premature aging. Ehret postulates that by removing mucus-forming foods from one's diet, many human illnesses can be healed and prevented.

Mucusless (also Mucus-Free): Refers to foods that are not mucus-forming. Such foods digest without leaving behind a thick, viscous, slimy substance called mucus. These foods include all kinds of fat-free and starchless fruits and vegetables.

Mucus-Forming: Refers to foods that create or leave behind uneliminated mucus in the human body. Such foods include meats, dairy, grains, starches, and fats.

Blood: The red fluid that flows through the veins and arteries of humans and other vertebrate animals, transporting oxygen to, and waste/carbon dioxide from, the tissues of the body.

Toxemia: An abnormal condition associated with the presence of toxic substances in the blood.

Vitality: Sometimes referred to as "vital force" in biological theory, refers to the force that animates and perpetuates life. Ehret's particular theory of vitality is expounded on in subsequent lessons, particularly Lesson V.

Naturopathy: Term coined in 1895 by John Scheel and made famous in the United States by one of Arnold Ehret's students named Benedict Lust, who founded the first school of naturopathy in 1902. Naturopathic medicine favors a holistic and drugless approach to healing and endeavors to employ the least invasive measures necessary to relieve symptoms and heal human illness.

Natural Hygiene (also Orthopathy): A healing philosophy derived from naturopathy that advocates plant-based diets, periods of intermittent fasting, and other lifestyle measures to address the symptoms of disease.

Medical science (Allopathic Medicine): The branch of science concerned with the study of the diagnosis, treatment, and prevention of disease. "Allopathic medicine" is an expression used by many proponents of natural healing to refer to mainstream medical use of pharmacology or physical interventions to treat or suppress symptoms of disease.

Fasting: To abstain from the intake of food and drink. It may also refer to various forms of dietary restriction, which include abstaining from solid foods (juice or liquid fasting), mucus-forming foods (mucusless diet), animal products, and so forth. Fasting may also refer more broadly to abstaining from modern conveniences or unnatural additions, such as a *fast* from electricity or the use of electronics for a period of time.

Disease: Ehret defines disease, or human illness, as an effort of the body to eliminate waste, mucus, and toxemias. Ehret does not purport to "treat" diseases, but to heal human illness through his *Healing System*.

Practitioner: Within the mucus-free community, this term is often used to identify a person who practices, or endeavors to perform, the *Mucusless Diet Healing System* as a lifestyle. This is distinct from the use of the term to identify the practice of a professional in a specialized field (e.g., *a legal practitioner*).

Review Questions: Lesson I

1. How does Arnold Ehret define disease?

2. How does Ehret define constipation?

3. About how many pounds of uneliminated fecal matter is in the typical person?

4. According to Ehret, humans can be healed by using special menus or radical fasts. (True or False)

5. According to Ehret, what is "Nature's infallible law and omnipotent healing process"?

6. Ehret says, "whatever simple reason cannot grasp is humbug, however scientific it may sound." What do you think is meant by this statement?

7. Why are Fasting and the Mucusless Diet often not successful in many cases?

Lesson II
Latent, Acute, and Chronic Diseases—
No Longer a Mystery

Summary: Lesson II

In Lesson II, Prof. Arnold Ehret elaborates on the nature of disease-causing substances, including mucus, foreign matter, uric acid, drugs, etc. First, he argues that the medical profession's use of drugs only addresses symptoms and fails to address the root causes, which are destructive dietary and living habits. Second, he infers that the residue of drugs is not eliminated from the body without the aid of mucus-free detoxification methods, and he cautions that negative symptoms may occur when old drug residues leave the body during the cleansing process. Third, Ehret explores the nature of latent, acute, and chronic disease, and how understanding these stages is necessary for an informed practice of the *Mucusless Diet Healing System*. Finally, Ehret contends that the *Mucusless Diet Healing System* can and will help prevent and heal all of the aforementioned stages of human illness.

Outline: Lesson II

1) What Are the Contents of Human Disease/Illness?

   a) Mucus, toxemias, uric acid, toxins, drugs, etc.

      i) Drugs are never fully eliminated. They are stored in the body for decades unless purged.

         (1) When the chemical poisons of drugs are dissolved and taken back into the circulation to be eliminated through the kidneys, unpleasant symptoms may include:

            (a) Extreme nervousness,

            (b) Dizziness,

            (c) Excessive heartbeats, and

            (d) Other strange miscellaneous symptoms.

      ii) Lack of food is often blamed for symptoms caused by the elimination of old drugs/medication trapped in the body, instead of the old drugs.

2) What is Latent Disease/Illness?

   a) Ehret asserts that the average person, considered healthy, has a stored-up accumulation of toxic waste in their bodies.

      i) Eventually this accumulation of waste might emerge as latent illness.

   b) When latent illness is stirred up, e.g. by a cold, great amounts of mucus may be expelled.

      i) People are often unhappy with Nature's cleansing process.

         (1) Cold- and flu-like symptoms indicate Nature's cleansing processes going deeper.

      ii) The body makes an effort to free the most vital organs from its waste.

3) What is Acute Disease/Illness? How Does It Become Chronic?

   a) An illness of short duration.

   b) The medical profession has many names for different ailments.

      i) In 2007, the World Health Organization distinguished over 12,420 disease categories. This number increases every year.

      ii) Drugs are often used to suppress symptoms while patients continue to eat poorly.

         (1) This prevents Nature from healing the body and promotes chronic illness in the patient.

            (a) The word chronic is derived from the Greek word *chronos*, meaning time.

Glossary: Lesson II

Latent disease: Illness that is hidden, dormant, and/or inactive.

Acute disease (Acute illness): Ehret uses the term acute disease to refer to any illness that develops quickly, is intense or severe, and lasts a relatively short period of time. If a condition lasts for a substantial period of time, it is considered chronic.

Chronic illness: An illness that takes a long time to heal. In medical science, a chronic illness is defined by an illness that lasts longer than 3 months.

Cold- and flu-like symptoms: In allopathic medicine, a "cold" refers to a viral infectious disease of the upper respiratory tract. Flu refers to an infectious disease caused by the influenza virus. Ehret challenges the notion that "viruses" are the primary cause of these ailments. Rather, he proposes that such illnesses can only occur in a body encumbered with mucus and other waste materials. The symptoms associated with colds and flu are viewed by Ehret as the way in which the body endeavors to eliminate disease-causing internal waste materials. Symptoms may include fever, runny nose, sore throat, muscle pains, coughing, headache, fatigue, diarrhea, body aches, vomiting, etc.

Elimination: Removal of physiological waste and encumbrances. The term is also used instead of the word "sick" by Mucusless Diet practitioners to identify short or extended periods of intensive waste elimination. In common parlance, a practitioner may say, "I'm going through an intense elimination today!" meaning that he or she is presumably eliminating large quantities of waste and experiencing various symptoms of human illness. Instances of elimination usually spur a practitioner to detoxify, fast, or abstain from mucus-forming foods. Extreme periods of elimination may be called a "healing crisis."

Healing crisis: The term "healing crisis" is a commonly used and related naturopathic term that refers to a period of intensive physical and emotional cleansing. Common symptoms include the expectoration of various colors of mucus from all orifices, fever, aches and pains, headaches, dizziness and vertigo, mood swings, diarrhea, vomiting, loss of appetite, depression or anxieties, heart palpitations, localized pain at the area of obstruction, etc.

Review Questions: Lesson II

1. Drugs always eventually eliminate from the body after taken. (True or False) Explain.

2. Describe what happens when dissolved chemical poisons from drugs are taken back into the circulation.

3. What is the difference between latent and acute illness/disease?

4. What happens when latent disease matter is stirred up in the body?

5. What are the contents of human disease/illness, according to Ehret?

6. What do cold- and flu-like symptoms indicate?

Lesson III
Why the Diagnosis?

Summary: Lesson III

In Lesson III, Ehret explores what may be called the "*Mucusless Diet Healing System* diagnosis," or "Ehret's diagnostic methods." Ehret uses the word *diagnosis* to mean the interpretation of health issues based on observable physiological factors. The aim of Ehret's approach is to 1) determine the amount and type of waste in the system, 2) if internal tissues or organs are decomposing, and 3) how far vitality has been compromised. Ehret critiques both medical and naturopathic diagnostic methods, concluding that they do not shed light on the source of the problem: pus- and mucus-forming foods. He reiterates that the name of any given disease, whether provided by medical or naturopathic authorities, is not particularly important. Rather, understanding the nature of the patient's internal uncleanliness is of primary importance. Finally, Ehret explains that it is critical to consider the condition of the patient's colon. Based on evidence given by experts in autopsy, Ehret explains that it is common for foreign matters to exist in the colon, including worms and decades-old feces-stones, along with over 10 to 15 pounds of uneliminated fecal matter. Ehret proposes that the Mucusless Diet Healing System is the best therapeutic method designed to effectively cleanse the colon and the entire body.

Outline: Lesson III

1) Why the Diagnosis?

   a) Some natural healing experts feel there is no need for diagnosis or individualized recommendations.

      i) Ehret asserts, "No other cure requires so much individual specialization and continual changing to meet the reaction of the patient."

   b) Fruit diet and fasting have a bad reputation because people who have not been successful failed to understand the importance of individualized diagnosis

      i) Neither Ehret nor the editor of this book purports to "diagnose" medical diseases.

         (1) Ehret uses the word diagnosis to simply mean the interpretation of health issues based upon observable physiological factors.

2) Promiscuous Fasting

   a) Many fasting enthusiasts dangerously advise fasting as applicable to all cases.

      i) After observing thousands of fasters, Ehret asserts that fasting requires individualized analysis and specific recommendations for each case.

3) Method of Constitutional Diagnosis

   a) The aim of Ehret's diagnostic methods is to determine:

      i) The relative amount of waste in the system.

      ii) The prominent type of waste.

         (1) Mucus, poisons, parasites, etc.

      iii) If pus is present in the system, how much, and if drugs were used.

      iv) If internal tissue or organs are in the processes of decomposition.

      v) How far vitality is lowered.

   b) General appearance, especially of the face, will also help indicate the internal condition.

4) Medical Diagnosis

   a) Ehret asserts, "Medical diagnosis throws no real light on the subject" of human illness.

      i) It is composed of a series of reports of symptoms and schemes of experiences tied to thousands of diseases.

      ii) "The name of the disease does not concern us at all."

5) Naturopathic Concepts

   a) It is an advance over medicine in teaching that disease is constitutional.

      i) However, it does not sufficiently explain that the source of illness is "foreign matter" in from uneliminated, unnatural foods.

6) Uric Diagnosis

a) Analysis of the urine is considered important by medical practitioners, but is misunderstood.

    i) The uric canal is the main avenue of elimination.

    ii) As soon as one fasts or improves their diet, waste can be found in the urine.

        (1) An analysis of this urine would be alarming!

b) "Whatever the body expels is waste, decayed, dead . . ."

7) How It Looks in the Human Colon

a) It is important to learn the condition of the inside of the patient's colon.

b) Experts in autopsy state that 60% to 70% of the colons examined have foreign matter, worms, and decades-old feces-stones.

    i) The inside walls of the over-intestines are often encrusted by old, hardened feces.

        (1) Like a filthy stovepipe or clogged kitchen sink pipe.

c) Ehret had obese patients that eliminated as much as 50 to 60 pounds of waste.

    i) 10 to 15 pounds from the colon alone.

d) The average so-called "healthy" person carries around pounds of never-eliminated feces.

    i) One "good stool" a day means nothing.

    ii) An overweight and sick person is in fact a living "cesspool" of waste that needs to cleanse using principles of the mucusless diet.

        (1) This includes many people who have already tried "nature cures."

Glossary: Lesson III

Diagnosis: The art or act of determining a disease or illness from its symptoms and observable signs.

Ehret's Diagnostic Method: The art of analyzing the internal uncleanliness of the body.

Pus: Refers to a thick white, yellowish, or greenish opaque liquid produced in infected tissue, consisting of dead white blood cells, bacteria, tissue debris, and serum. It also refers to the substance that dead animal flesh is chemically changed to after being consumed or while rotting.

Uric: Pertaining to, contained in, or derived from urine.

Albumen: A class of simple, water-soluble proteins that can be coagulated by heat and are found in egg whites, blood serum, milk, and many other animal and plant tissues. Albuminous refers to something consisting of, resembling, or containing albumen. Albuminous foods decompose into pus inside the body.

Fruit diet: A diet consisting primarily of fruit. Among people that identify themselves as exclusive fruit eaters, there is disagreement on whether certain items that are technically "fruits," but often viewed and used as vegetables, should be included. Given that there are some fruits that are mucus-forming, Ehret's work suggests that he is referencing mucus-free fruits when he says "fruit diet."

Cesspool: Any filthy receptacle, disgusting place, or container for the temporary storage of liquid waste and sewage.

Review Questions: Lesson III

1. What does Ehret mean by the word "diagnosis"?

2. Healing with the Mucusless Diet requires individual specialization for each patient. (True or False). Why or why not?

3. What happens to human urine when a cleansing diet is applied, or fasting practiced?

4. What can be found in the colons of many people who have never cleansed?

5. Why does Ehret compare the human intestine to a filthy stovepipe?

6. What is the aim of Ehret's method of constitutional diagnosis?

7. What is pus? What is albumen?

Lesson IV
The Diagnosis—Part 2

Summary: Lesson IV

In Lesson IV, Prof. Arnold Ehret introduces his theory of two primary physiological body types, fat and lean. They are based on the way in which a particular physiology copes with digesting and eliminating mucus- and pus-forming foods. Fat types are more mechanically obstructed and often overeaters of starchy foods. People with this physiology can easily put on weight. Lean types are characterized by having an inordinate amount of toxic waste, acidity, uric acid, and pus in their systems. The latter are generally one-sided meat eaters. The overeating of pus and mucus in this type results in the body breaking down the waste into toxic chemicals, some of which remain uneliminated until detoxification. Ehret also expounds on his diagnostic methods, suggesting that a short fast is one of the best ways to reveal the condition of the patient. He examines a number of common illnesses, including colds, pneumonia, toothaches, rheumatism, gout, mental illness, diseases of the sex organs, etc., and shows how they are all caused by the same general and constitutional encumbrances of the body.

Outline: Lesson IV

1) Fat and Lean Physiological Types

    a) Fat Type

        i) The bodily mechanism is mechanically more obstructed.

            (1) Often an overeater of starchy foods.

    b) Lean Type

        i) The bodily mechanism endures more chemical interference.

            (1) Often a one-sided meat-eater.

                (a) This way of eating produces much acidity, uric acid, other poisons, and pus.

2) Disease Story

    a) Questions Ehret asks his prospective patients:

        i) How long have you been sick?

        ii) What did the doctor call your disease?

        iii) What was the nature of the treatment?

        iv) How much and what kinds of treatment was taken?

        v) Have you ever been operated on?

        vi) What other kinds of treatment have you taken before?

    b) What are the most important issues?

        i) The patient's current diet.

        ii) Special craving for certain foods.

        iii) Bad living habits.

        iv) If constipated, how long.

    c) Ehret asserts that it is important to base a change in diet on the patient's present diet.

        i) "Only a SLIGHT CHANGE toward an improved diet" is recommended at first.

3) The Experimental Diagnosis

    a) A short fast is the most exact and unerring diagnosis.

        i) The quicker a patient feels "worse," the greater and more poisonous his or her encumbrance.

        ii) If they become dizzy, suffer headaches, etc., they are greatly clogged with mucus and toxemias.

        iii) Ehret's prognosis of disease:

            (1) A short fast exposes the nature and location of physiological weaknesses and indicates how one might become sick in the future.

(a) In other words, it can expose the nature of one's latent illnesses.

4) Some Special Diagnoses

    a) Ehret shows that all illnesses, even more severe cases, are caused by the same general constitutional encumbrances and congestion of the body.

        i) Examples include a cold, pneumonia, toothaches, boils, sex diseases, mental diseases, etc.

           (1) Ehret found that anyone with a mental illness has congestion of the brain.

               (a) "There is nothing easier to heal by fasting than insanity . . ."

               (b) "If something is wrong with anyone, look first to the stomach."

               (c) "The mentally diseased man or woman suffers physiologically from gas pressure on the brain."

Glossary: Lesson IV

Physiology: Refers to the investigation and description of natural entities and the normal function of living organisms.

Physiological types: Arnold Ehret identifies two kinds of human physiologies: fat and lean types. These types refer to the way in which one's body copes with digesting and eliminating mucus- and pus-forming foods. Fat types are mechanically more obstructed and often overeaters of starchy foods. Their bodies tuck the uneliminated waste into the tissue system away from the heart and lungs, and when large amounts of uneliminated mucus are in the body, they become obese. Lean types are characterized by having an inordinate amount of toxic waste, uric acid, and pus in the body and are generally one-sided meat eaters. The overeating of pus and mucus in this type results in the body breaking down the waste into very toxic chemicals that remain uneliminated until detoxification.

Ehret's prognosis of disease: Prognosis is the forecast of the likely course of an illness. Ehret asserts that a short fast may reveal a person's physiological weaknesses and indicate where and how they will become sick in the future if the wrong methods of living persist. Ehret states that the tongue can be used as a mirror to observe the general condition of the entire membrane system and that it is a more effective diagnostic tool than other medical and naturopathic approaches.

Review Questions: Lesson IV

1. Name and describe the two body types identified by Ehret.

2. Which physiological type is often a one-sided meat eater?

3. When examining a patient's "disease story," what are the primary questions you should ask?

4. What are the most important issues to consider regarding someone's "disease story"?

5. According to Ehret, what is the most exact and unerring way to experimentally examine a patient's condition?

6. Describe Ehret's thoughts about mental illness.

Lesson IVa
The Magic Mirror

Summary: Lesson IVa

In Lesson IVa, Arnold Ehret discusses his "magic mirror" diagnostic tool, which consists of analyzing the surface of the tongue during or after a short period of fasting. A tongue coated with slime indicates a degree of congestion throughout the body. His general prognosis of disease is that everyone, even seemingly healthy people, have latent illnesses only waiting for the opportunity to be purged from the body. When there is a shock to the system, for instance through cold- and flu-like symptoms, Ehret observes that so-called "civilized" humans often inhibit Nature's ability to heal by using drugs and continuing to eat pus- and mucus-forming foods.

Outlines: Lesson IVa

1) Supplement to Diagnosis

   a) Since humans degenerated through civilization, they no longer know what to do when sick.

      i) Disease is as much of a mystery today as it was to the ancient "medicine man."

         (1) Today the "germ" theory has replaced the "demon" concept (that of a malevolent outside force bent on doing someone harm).

2) The Magic Mirror

   a) Ehret identifies the tongue as the "magic mirror," a diagnostic tool that can show how congested someone's system is.

      i) It is a mirror of the entire membrane system.

         (1) A coated tongue is evidence of waste throughout the entire system.

         (2) If the tongue is coated during or after a short fast, this indicates congestion in the system.

         (3) After a fast it is advisable to eat only mucus-free foods to allow the body to eliminate the waste.

3) The Healing Process

   a) Every disease is constitutional constipation.

      i) Even the microscopically small capillaries are chronically constipated because of generations of eating pus- and mucus-forming foods.

   b) Ehret asserts that all humans have large quantities of waste in their blood.

      i) The waste from protein and starch are sticky and clog the body.

   c) The tissues of the body and internal organs are similar to a sponge.

      i) Imagine a sponge soaked in paste or glue.

         (1) How hard would it be to rid it of the sticky substances? How would you do it?

   d) Ehret asserts that the field of naturopathy must cleanse its science from medical superstitions.

      i) Nature, alone, is the teacher of truth.

   e) Medicine has devised laboratory tests, e.g., urinalysis, blood tests, etc.

      i) Ehret asserts that these tests do not actually assess the amount of constitutional encumbrances in the body.

         (1) Ehret argues that these tests are a fallacy.

         (2) Ehret notes hundreds of cases where patients went to multiple doctors and were diagnosed with different diseases by each.

         (3) Ehret exclaims "I know exactly what ails you—through facial diagnosis—and you will see it yourself in the 'magic mirror' within a few days."

f) Meat decomposes into pus, and thus it is "pus-forming."

g) If a diabetic patient is fed eggs, meat, bacon, etc., then they are starved from the lack of natural, sugar-containing foods such as fruit.

4) The Experimental Diagnosis

    a) After a 2- to 3-day fast, the tongue will indicate the appearance of the inside of the body.

        i) The breath will indicate the grade of decomposition.

    b) If there is pain felt in any one place, this is a weak point.

    c) Waste will show up in the urine with clouds of mucus.

        i) Mucus will be expelled from the nose, throat, lungs, and feces.

    d) The experimental diagnosis reveals the problem and how to solve it:

        i) Through a moderate transition diet or more radical one.

        ii) Whether or not to continue or discontinue the fast.

    e) If there are symptoms of nervousness or heart trouble, the patient likely has drugs stored in their body.

    f) All other diagnoses, including iris-diagnosis, examination of the spine, etc., are never exact and not dependable.

5) The Prognosis of Disease

    a) Everyone, no matter how healthy they may seem, has a latent sickness.

        i) Nature awaits an opportunity to eliminate the waste stored up since childhood.

    b) People fail to understand that a shock to the system, such as through a cold or flu, is Nature's way of cleansing the body.

        i) People are unable to heal naturally due to the use of drugs, etc.

            (1) This can cause one's illness to become chronic.

    c) The prognosis may be made after several days of fasting through analysis of the magic mirror and location of "weak points."

    d) Fasting until the tongue is clean is dangerous.

        i) It is important to put the magic mirror analysis into proper perspective and not obsess over it.

        ii) Ehret says, "For the ordinary person, it will require from 1 to 3 years of systematically continued fasting and natural, cleansing diet before the body is actually cleansed of 'foreign matters.'"

            (1) This statement is often misinterpreted to mean that it will only take 1 to 3 years to reach the highest levels of a mucusless lifestyle. In actuality, transitioning for 1 to 3 years is only the beginning of the process.

            (2) After 1 to 3 years, the patient will see how waste is constantly eliminating from:

(a) The urinary canal

(b) The colon

(c) The eyes, ears, nose, and throat

(d) Every pore of the skin

    (i) Dandruff is dry mucus eliminating.

Glossary: Lesson IVa

Magic Mirror: A term coined by Arnold Ehret to describe a diagnostic method of analyzing the surface of the tongue during or after a fast to deduce the level of internal uncleanliness.

Review Questions: Lesson IVa

1. What is the magic mirror? How is the magic mirror used with Ehret's "Experimental Diagnosis"?

2. It will take about 21 days of fasting and natural diet to totally cleanse the body of "foreign matter." (True or False) Explain.

3. According to Ehret, what does meat decompose into in the body?

4. Why is it dangerous to try and fast until the tongue is clean?

5. According to Ehret, what negative effects can result from taking drugs when sick?

Lesson V
The Formula of Life

Summary: Lesson V

In Lesson V, Arnold Ehret presents his theory of the "formula of life," represented by the equation Vitality (V) equals Power (P) minus Obstruction (O), or $V = P - O$. Vitality stands for life. Power represents that which perpetuates life (the science of breath). Obstruction represents that which stifles Power, thereby stifling Vitality/life. Ehret identifies mucus-forming foods as the primary cause of Obstruction in the human organism. When Obstruction becomes greater than Power, the human engine (body) comes to a standstill. He establishes a new framework in which to view the human body through his assertion that it is an "air-gas engine" powered primarily by oxygen through the process of breathing. He challenges the standard view of the heart and lungs with his proposition that the lungs are the body's "pump" and the heart is the valve. Given that the body is indeed an "air-gas engine," and Obstruction is that which inhibits the body from fully utilizing air, Ehret affirms that our diets should consist of foods that help the body eliminate Obstruction while leaving behind as little waste as possible. Ehret proposes that mucus-free foods are the best foods to help remove waste (Obstruction) so that the body can fully utilize oxygen (Power), thereby resulting in an unobstructed and disease-free life.

29

Outline: Lesson V

1) The Secret of Vitality

   a) Ehret explains, "V = P − O (V equals P minus O) is the formula of life—and at the same time, you may call it the formula of death."

      i) V stands for Vitality.

         (1) Life.

      ii) P stands for Power.

         (1) That which perpetuates the life of the body.

      iii) O stands for Obstruction.

         (1) Bodily encumbrance that slows or halts the proper function of the body.

         (2) When O (Obstruction) becomes greater than P (Power), the human machine comes to a standstill (i.e., death).

   b) An engineer calculates E = P − F (Energy equals Power minus Friction).

      i) If an engine has too much friction, it will not run properly.

         (1) How far will a car's engine travel if its gas and oil tanks are filled with sand instead of oil and gas?

      ii) If this idea is transferred to the body, then mucus, pus, toxic waste, etc., create friction/obstruction in the body causing it to function improperly.

   c) Ehret endeavors to teach a "New Physiology" based on the correction of medical errors.

2) Human Body as an Air-Gas Engine

   a) "The human engine must first be seen before all other physiological considerations as an air-gas engine."

      i) Most of the body is constructed of rubber-like, elastic, spongy material called flesh and tissues.

   b) The body is a pump system operated through air pressure.

      i) This pump system circulates internal liquids such as the blood and other fluids.

         (1) The lungs are the pump and the heart is the valve—and not the opposite.

   c) Atmospheric outside counter-pressure works in harmony with the lungs.

      i) A vacuum is created in the lung cavity.

      ii) The human body functions automatically by inhaling air pressure and expelling chemically changed air.

   d) "The Latin word 'spira' means first air, and then spirit:"

      i) "'The breath of God' is in fact first, good fresh air!"

ii) "It has been said that breathing is life, and it is true that you develop vitality—health—through physical and breathing exercises."

e) Artificially speeding up the circulation can cause one to increase power at the expense of vitality.

   i) This happens if the elasticity of the body is lost.

   ii) Ehret does not recommend using artificial means to speed up the elimination of bodily waste.

3) Which Are the Best Foods?

a) According to Ehret's theory, the best foods would be those that help remove waste (Obstruction) while not leaving behind harmful residue (mucus-free foods).

b) Vitality does not depend directly on the "right diet."

   i) Eating too much of the best foods, especially in a body filled with waste, can be harmful.

      (1) If good foods are mixed with bad foods, it can be problematic.

      (2) In such cases the body cannot absorb the "efficiency-giving" vital substances of the foods.

c) It is worthless to figure out "food values" (nutritional values) with the intention of increasing vitality as long as the body is full of obstruction.

   i) This problem is solved through Ehret's gradual and systematic approach.

d) Why do fruit diets and extreme fasting methods fail?

   i) Because the inexperienced layperson attempts to move too rapidly and removes "O" (Obstruction) too fast.

   ii) They feel good for a while but then experience what some call a healing crisis.

      (1) Weakness, fatigue, etc.

   iii) They then fall back on the wrong diet.

e) Ehret emphasizes, "Few think as I do that Vitality, Energy and Strength are not derived from food at all!"

   i) Vitality does not derive primarily from food.

   ii) Artificially increasing "Power" through unnatural shaking or vibration is harmful.

      (1) This happens through extreme forms of exercise or treatments that dangerously shake the body.

   iii) The limit of how long a human can go without food is yet unknown.

f) Perhaps nitrogen from the air may be assimilated in a perfectly clean body.

   i) Implications of this idea challenge the protein theory.

Glossary: Lesson V

V = P − O (Vitality = Power − Obstruction): Equation devised by Arnold Ehret, which he calls the "formula of life." Ehret's proposition is that the human body is a perpetual-motion, air-gas engine powered exclusively by oxygen and that the body ceases to function when obstructed with waste. He asserts that mucus-forming foods create obstruction in the human body, and that a diet consisting of starchless/fat-free fruits and green-leaf vegetables is the only group of foods that do not leave behind obstructive residues in the body and will aid it during the process of natural healing.

Air-gas engine: Arnold Ehret identifies the human body to be an air-gas engine that is fundamentally powered through the process of breathing. Mucus- and pus-forming foods leave behind harmful residues in the body that create obstruction. When the human organism becomes too filled with obstructions and is unable to get oxygen to the blood, the body comes to a standstill. Thus, mucusless foods are identified to be the ones best fit for humans, as they leave behind the least amount of obstruction and aid the elimination of waste from the body.

Spirit: The word "spirit" is from the mid-thirteenth century, first meaning the "animating or vital principle in man and animals," the Old French *espirit*, and from Latin *spiritus*, meaning "soul, courage, vigor, breath," related to *spirare*, meaning "to breathe."

Review Questions: Lesson V

1. What does Ehret call the "Formula of Life"?

2. Explain what is meant by V = P − O.

3. According to Ehret, what kind of fuel does the human body run on?

4 Why does vitality not rely on only eating "the right foods"?

5. Extreme exercise and vibrating the body are important for eliminating internal waste (True or False). Why?

6. Why do patients often fall back onto a "wrong" mucus-forming diet after eating mucusless or after a long fast?

7. According to Ehret, the lungs act as a pump and heart as a valve. (True or False)

8. What happens to the human body when it has more "obstruction" than "power"?

Lesson VI
The New Physiology

Summary: Lesson VI

In Lesson VI, Arnold Ehret offers an introduction to his theory of the "New Physiology." He outlines commonly held concepts about human physiology, including blood circulation, metabolism, the need for high-protein foods, blood composition, and bloodbuilding. In this lesson he focuses on examining theories of blood circulation and metabolism. He asserts that the lungs function as a pump and the heart a valve, while offering examples to support his new framework. He redefines metabolism as primarily a process for the elimination of waste. He then explains that the concept of metabolism, as it is known in medical science, is wrong and dangerous. Ultimately, Ehret rejects modern nutritional ideals that instruct humans to "replace" proteins or fats through eating foods rich in these constituents.

Outline: Lesson VI

1) The Error of Blood Circulation

    a) Ehret asserts that medical science will never find the solution for human illness as long as it has the wrong concept of blood circulation.

        i) The lungs pump the blood which drives the heart, which is a valve.

            (1) As soon as breathing is increased, circulation and heart rate increase.

            (2) Heart rate increases when you take a stimulating poison, such as alcohol. It decreases if you take a paralyzing poison, such as digitalis (medicinal herb).

2) Metabolism

    a) Ehret explains that "metabolism, or the 'science of the change of matter,' is the most absurd and the most dangerous doctrine-teaching ever imposed on humankind."

        i) It is the foundation of the wrong cell theory and albumen theory.

            (1) Albumen replacement is unnecessary.

    b) Ehret says, "The erroneous idea that the cells of the body are continually used up by the process of life in their essential substance of protein and must be continually replaced by high-protein foods can be and is evidentially refuted by my investigations, experiments, and observations on some hundred fasters."

    c) What medicine calls "metabolism" is the elimination of waste by the body as soon as the stomach is empty.

        i) Medical and some naturopathic authorities believe you live off of your own flesh during a fast.

            (1) Ehret refutes this notion.

    d) Lean people can fast longer and more easily than more heavyset ones.

        i) Example: Hindu fakirs, who are often very skinny, are known for fasting for long periods of time.

            (1) Ehret explains that the cleaner the body is, the longer and more easily one can fast.

        ii) Ehret's world record of 49 days' fasting monitored by government officials could only have happened after a strict mucusless diet for a long period of time.

    e) The body does not eliminate a single cell that is in vital condition.

    f) The limit where real starvation sets in is yet unknown.

Glossary: Lesson VI

Metabolism: The chemical processes that take place inside a living organism in order to sustain life.

Albumen Theory: The albumen theory, or nitrogenous-albumin metabolic theory, purports that humans must eat protein-rich, pus- and mucus-forming foods to provide fuel for, rebuild, and sustain the body.

Additive Principle: The "additive principle" is a term used by modern-day practitioners of the *Mucusless Diet Healing System* to refer to the belief that humans need to consume, accumulate, and use various forms of material matter to exist. Modern theories of nutrition and metabolism emerge from an additive concept, whereby it is thought that the human body must take in and metabolize various elements not obtained through the process of breathing to live. Ehret rejects the foundation of the additive principle and proposes his "formula to life" (Vitality = Power − Obstruction), which asserts that human life exists as a result of the non-accumulation, and elimination, of unnecessary matter.

Review Questions: Lesson VI

1. According to Ehret, why does the circulation increase when running or climbing a mountain?

2. Why does Ehret find standard theories of metabolism to be "absurd"?

3. Why is it easier for internally clean people to fast?

4. How many days was Ehret's longest record-breaking fast?

5. What does Ehret's long fast prove or suggest?

Lesson VII
The New Physiology—Part 2

Summary: Lesson VII

In Lesson VII, Arnold Ehret challenges the theory that humans need to consume protein-rich foods to replace and maintain internal constituents of the body. He explains that high-protein foods act as a poisonous stimulant in humans and ultimately cause illness. This is due in part to the difficulty the body has eliminating protein-rich foods. He offers some logical examples to demonstrate the erroneous nature of standard dietetic theories, including the revelation that adult cows do not drink milk to produce milk, therefore why would humans need to eat animal flesh to produce their own flesh? He also points out that human physiologies are closer to those of our frugivorous primates, and that humans have lived healthier without food value formulas and nutritional concepts for thousands of years.

Outline: Lesson VII

1) High-Protein Foods

   a) When the movement for naturopathy and a meatless diet began in the 19th century, medical scientists were trying to prove that humans needed to replace protein daily.

      i) You now know that the source of Vitality, according to Ehret, is not protein-rich foods or a "balanced diet," but a body without waste.

   b) High-protein foods act as stimulation for a certain period of time.

      i) It is commonly known that dead animal substance becomes very poisonous as soon as it enters into oxidation with air.

   c) Educated people have endeavored to prove that humans are meat-eating animals.

      i) Although the descendant theory suggests that humans are frugivorous, like apes.

   d) Mother's milk only contains 2 ½ to 3 percent protein.

   e) The idea that humans must eat protein to build, grow, and maintain muscle is absurd.

      i) Is it necessary for an adult cow to drink milk to produce milk?

   f) Why can a one-sided meat eater live longer than a vegetarian starch-eater?

      i) The meat-eater creates less solid obstructions, although their latent diseases are more dangerous in the long run because they accumulate more poisons, pus, and uric acid.

   g) For thousands of years humans have lived healthier without food value/nutritional formulas.

      i) The entire proposition is a farce masquerading as so-called "science."

   h) Ehret found that in a clean, mucus-free body, the foods with the least protein—fruits— develop the highest energy and endurance.

      i) If nitrogen, the essential part of protein, is important, then it seems to Ehret that under ideal circumstances, it could be assimilated from the air.

   i) When we allow the body to become clogged up with mucus and other foreign matter, we may expect high blood pressure.

Glossary: Lesson VII

Stimulation: To temporarily increase the activity of an organism or its body organ. Ehret's proposition is that mucus-forming foods are not nurturing or "nutritious," but serve only to unnaturally stimulate the body like a poisonous drug.

Protein: From Fr. *protéine*, coined 1838 by Dutch chemist Gerhard Johan Mulder (1802–1880), perhaps on suggestion of Berzelius, from Gk. *proteios* "the first quality [principle]," from *protos* "first" (see proto-). Originally a theoretical substance thought to be essential to life. Today, the common definition is the protein is any of a class of nitrogenous organic compounds that consist of large molecules composed of one or more long chains of amino acids. Further, the plant or animal tissue rich in such molecules, considered as a food source.

Review Questions: Lesson VII

1. High-protein foods act as _____ for a certain period of time. (Fill in the blank).

2. According to Ehret, when people become sick, it is important that they eat high-protein foods to maintain their strength. (True or False) Why or why not?

3. According to Ehret, what type of food are humans biologically designed to eat?

4. It is a widely known fact that cows drink milk and eat the flesh of other cows to help them produce their own milk and flesh (beef). (True or False) Why or why not?

5. According to Ehret, why can a one-sided meat eater sometimes live longer than a vegetarian over-eater?

6. Why can a one-sided meat eater sometimes live longer than a vegetarian over-eater?

Lesson VIII
The New Physiology—Part 3

Summary: Lesson VIII

In Lesson VIII, Arnold Ehret continues the discussion of his "New Physiology" theory, focusing on blood composition. First, he aligns himself with the theories of Dr. Thomas Powell, who affirms that what medical scientists called "white blood corpuscles" is actually waste, or "pathogens," in the blood. Ehret surmises that one reason white blood cells are considered normal is that all people eating a standard diet of civilization will have them in excess. Ehret points out that what medical science identifies as "normal" or good health is a pathological condition, including the constituents of the blood. Second, he hypothesized that paler skin is the result of the body having become saturated with mucus-based waste. He observed how much darker his skin became while living for an extended period of time on a mucusless diet, and how he grew paler after eating mucus-forming foods, such as a piece of bread. Third, Ehret examines the role of iron in the blood and how its red color is due to iron oxide rust. Finally, Ehret outlines tests that truth-seekers can perform to better understand the nature of mucus- and acid-forming foods.

41

Outline: Lesson VIII

1) Blood Composition

   a) Ehret asserts that the understanding of human physiology by medical scientists of his day has many errors.

   b) Ehret's question: Are the so-called white blood corpuscles living cells of vital importance or are they waste, mucus, and/or "pathogens" as Thomas Powell calls them?

      i) Ehret agrees with Dr. Thomas Powell that what were called "white corpuscles" in the early 1900s were waste from high-protein and starchy foods.

      ii) As evidence, Ehret points considers several logical examples:

        (1) White corpuscles are increased during disease.

        (2) They are increased at the site of disease.

        (3) They are also increased during digestion, especially of high-protein foods.

      iii) Medical "science" considers white corpuscles as a normal condition of health since everyone has them.

        (1) There is no person today without excess mucus in their body from unelimated, unnatural food substances.

   c) In his first book, Ehret hypothesized that light colored skin is the result of the body being overfilled with mucus-based waste for generations.

      i) Ehret explains, "Everybody knows that an extreme case of paleness is a 'bad sign.'"

      ii) Ehret recalled that his skin became so dark that people thought he was from India.

        (1) Ehret claims this was due to the prevalence of red blood.

        (2) He noticed his skin getting paler as soon as he ate something like a piece of bread.

      iii) Ehret recommends that anyone who wants to read further about the theories of "white blood" as waste, see Dr. Thomas Powell's book, *Fundamentals and Requirements of Health and Disease* (1909).

   d) The two most important factors:

      i) The importance and role of iron in the human body and blood.

      ii) The presence of "sugar-stuff" in the blood.

   e) Ehret's observations about blood:

      i) The red color of blood is due to iron oxide (i.e., rust).

      ii) The sugar-stuff in blood is of high importance and part of the perfect blood hemoglobin.

        (1) In a clean state, blood will become thick as soon as it comes into contact with the atmosphere/oxygen.

          (a) See *Rational Fasting* for Ehret's experimentation on his own blood and how he could get wounds to heal immediately.

f) One truth found by science: acidity is a sign of disease.

   i) It is not surprising that the mixed-eater's body becomes acidic.

g) Ehret's Acidic & Mucus-Forming Diet Test

   i) Eat a regular dinner and then get it out of your stomach an hour later to observe the sour fermenting mixture of terrible odor.

      (1) It is not actually advisable to perform this test.

   ii) A better personal test:

      (1) Create a meal for an invisible guest. Empty that portion into a cooking vessel.

      (2) Stir well.

      (3) Then cook in an oven at 98 degrees for 30 minutes.

      (4) Remove and place a cover over the vessel and leave sitting overnight.

         (a) Could also be sealed in a Ziploc bag.

      (5) A distinct surprise will await you in the morning when you open the container.

         (a) Notice the slimy nature due to the pus- and mucus-forming foods, and the terrible odor.

Glossary: Lesson VIII

Blood: The red fluid that flows through the veins and arteries of humans and other vertebrate animals, transporting oxygen to, and waste/carbon dioxide from, the tissues of the body.

Acidosis: A condition in which there is too much acid in the body fluids. According to Ehret, such acid is often derived from uneliminated pus- and mucus-forming foods.

Rust: A reddish coating of iron oxide that is formed on iron or steel by oxidation, especially in the presence of moisture.

Iron oxides: Chemical compounds composed of iron and oxygen. Iron oxides and oxide-hydroxides are prevalent in Nature, play a vital role in many environmental and biological processes, and are broadly used by humans, e.g., as iron ores, pigments, catalysts, and hemoglobin.

Hemoglobin: (General definition) An iron-containing respiratory pigment of vertebrate red blood cells made up of a globin composed of four subunits, each of which is linked to a heme molecule, that functions in oxygen transport to the tissues after conversion to oxygenated form in the gills or lungs, and that assists in carbon dioxide transport back to the gills or lungs after surrender of its oxygen.

Review Questions: Lesson VIII

1. The oxidation of iron in the blood causes it to turn it become what color?

2. Dr. Thomas Powell and Arnold Ehret both believe that white blood corpuscles defend the body. (True or False) Explain.

3. According to Ehret, how do mucus and toxemias affect the color of the skin?

4. What happens to mucus-forming foods when they sit for long periods of time in the intestines?

5. What is the name of a book written by Julius Hensel referenced by Arnold Ehret in the Mucusless Diet Healing System?

Further Reading: Lesson VIII

Powell, Thomas. 1909. *Fundamentals and Requirements of Health and Disease*. Los Angeles: Powell Publishing.

Hensel, Julius, and Charles A. Schindler. 1967. *Life: Its Foundation and the Means for Its Preservation; A Physical Explanation for the Practical Application of Agriculture, Forestry, Nutrition, the Functions of Life, Health and Disease and General Welfare*. Hergiswil, CH: C. Schindler.

Lesson IX
The New Physiology—Part 4

Summary: Lesson IX

In Lesson IX, Arnold Ehret concludes the discussion of his "New Physiology" by discussing his thoughts on bloodbuilding. He explains that a primary goal of his Mucusless Diet methodology is to create perfect human blood. He reasons that clean blood is necessary to help dissolve and eliminate the waste and poisons concealed in the body. He asserts that animal-based foods are not only unnecessary for the human body, but that they do not create human blood and eventually result in illness. He points out that herbivores, such as cows, can build their bodies through grass alone. Ultimately, Ehret proposes that humans are naturally fruit eaters and that the sugar from fruits helps create perfect human blood.

Outline: Lesson IX

1) Bloodbuilding

   a) One's health and disease depend almost entirely on diet.

   b) Which foods build natural, good blood, and which do not?

      i) Ehret's methods work by endeavoring to create perfect blood that:

         (1) Dissolves and eliminates waste and poisons.

   c) What medical science teaches regarding bloodbuilding is "doubly wrong."

      i) Wrong about the chemistry of the body,

      ii) Wrong based on the truth of Nature.

   d) The authors that started physiological science lacked knowledge of chemistry due to a more humanistic education.

      i) Protein became a fundamentally misleading concept.

         (1) They reasoned that muscles, tissues, and the body's essential substance are protein; therefore, protein must be introduced into the bloodstream to build and grow the body.

            (a) Namely, you must "eat muscles to build muscles, you must eat fat to build fat," etc.

               (i) Does a nursing mother need to drink milk to produce milk?

      ii) These theories are followed by the average mixed-eater.

      iii) To take an inorganic iron, lime, etc., to try and replace it in the body is a similar error.

   e) Cows build flesh, tissues, bones, hair, milk, etc., from grass alone.

      i) Feeding milk to a cow to increase milk production would be ridiculous.

         (1) Yet, this is the erroneous logic applied to the human body.

   f) Today, every substance of the human body is chemically analyzed.

      i) Doctors dream of perfecting a chemically concentrated food substance to be able to carry your meal in your pocket.

         (1) This will not happen, as the body does not assimilate a single atom of food not derived from the vegetable or fruit kingdom.

         (2) All manufactured and processed foods do not build human blood, and only "stimulate."

   g) Animal-based foods cannot build human blood.

      i) Because humans are naturally fruit eaters.

         (1) Does the juice of a ripe blackberry, cherry, or black grape not resemble blood?

            (a) Can half-decayed muscle tissue build better blood?

(b) As soon as the animal is killed, it is in decomposition.

    ii)   Albumen (from high-protein animal products like eggs) is not the most important substance for the blood.

  h) Ehret explains that the most important substance for humans is fruit sugar (carbon hydrate).

    i)   Fruits and vegetables.

    ii)   Science even shows that the small amount of protein needed is developed from grape-sugar (fruit sugar).

      (1) Vegetable-eating animals transformed these foods.

    iii) Whoever does not understand Vitality = Power − Obstruction, will never believe the truth of human nourishment.

  i) As soon as the blood is improved through fruits, the average person immediately starts the elimination of obstructions and feels better for a period of time.

    i)   But, when more waste is dissolved and the body shocked from obstruction in the circulation, the lack of nutritious food is blamed.

      (1) They return to "regular foods," become stimulated (in other words, drugged), and feel better for a while.

        (a) Illness may eventually return, and do so chronically.

Glossary: Lesson IX

Carbon hydrates: More commonly referred to as carbohydrates, carbon hydrates are any of a large class of organic compounds consisting of carbon, hydrogen, and oxygen. They are produced in green plants by photosynthesis. Sugars, starches, and cellulose are all carbohydrates. For Ehret, the highest forms of carbohydrate-containing foods for humans include fresh, fat-free fruits derived of simple sugars.

Grape sugar, or fruit sugar, or fructose: A very sweet monosaccharide sugar naturally occurring in many fruits and honey.

Review Questions: Lesson IX

1. According to Ehret, what kind of foods creates vital human blood?

2. Most carnivorous animals in Nature cook their foods in order to be able to digest them. (True or False) Explain.

3. Clean blood is able to dissolve and eliminate waste better than obstructed blood. (True or False) Explain.

4. According to Ehret, why are processed foods of all kinds unhealthy?

Lesson X
Critique of all Other Healing Systems and Unbiased, Unprejudiced Reviews

Summary: Lesson X

In Lesson X, Arnold Ehret considers positive and negative elements of various healing practices. He divides healing disciplines into two main categories, namely medicine and drugless healing. Ehret explains that "quacks" often promulgated dangerous remedies, some of which became standardized within medical science. He affirms that modern serums are no better than the dangerous preparations of old, despite being "scientifically prepared." Ehret explains that medical practices serve to suppress disease symptoms with drugs. Ehret then outlines and discusses three classes of drugless healing, including physical treatments, mental treatments, and dietetic treatments. Physical treatments include exercise, stretching, breath work, chiropractic, massage, physical therapy, etc. He explains that such treatments can relieve symptoms, but never fully heal as long as a pus- and mucus-forming diet is continued. Ehret finds mental treatments, like psychotherapy, to have the advantage of not prescribing drugs. However, he explains that such mental treatments remain ignorant of the foundation of disease, and therefore limit its effectiveness.

Outline: Lesson X

1) Medicine and Drugless Healing

   a) There are many methods of "healing," which may be divided into two different classes: medicine and drugless healing.

2) Medicine

   a) Ehret explains that, historically, mysterious inventions were developed by quacks.

      i) Using mercury was once a standard "remedy" developed by quacks.

      ii) The modern serums, etc., are not better, although thought to be "scientifically prepared."

      iii) Medicine is able to often "suppress" symptoms but not heal.

        (1) If a new and dangerous poison is introduced into the circulation of a sick person, the elimination is more or less stopped because the body instinctively sets to work on neutralizing the new poisons.

        (2) Symptoms come back as soon as the life is saved.

3) Drugless Healing

   a) Can be divided into three kinds:

      i) Physical treatments, mental treatments, dietetic treatments.

   b) Physical treatments.

      i) All have a tendency to loosen local constitutional encumbrances through vibrations and thermal differences.

        (1) The Kneipp cure, for example, uses cold compresses to stimulate the circulation and elimination.

      ii) General examples:

        (1) exercise, stretching, breathing exercises, massage, osteopathy, physical therapy, electricity, electric light, sunlight, etc.

        (2) Chiropractic can give immediate relief from pain, but it usually returns sooner or later if the adjustments are discontinued.

          (a) Ehret has witnessed deformed spines improve through fasting.

      iii) These methods can relieve symptoms but never fully heal as long as they do not improve the patient's diet.

   c) Mental treatments.

      i) It has been proven that the condition of the mind has a major influence on our health.

        (1) Fear, sorrows, and worries have a bad influence not only on heart and nerves, but circulation, digestion, etc.

      ii) Psychotherapy, mental and divine healing, Christian Science, etc., have one advantage:

        (1) They usually do not prescribe drugs.

(2) However, they can keep people in ignorance about what disease really is.

(3) It is farcical and pitiful to pray to a Creator for a miraculous healing while rejecting and disregarding real divine foods—the fruits of paradise ("bread of heaven").

(4) It is hard to believe in mental healing knowing that the average chronically sick person is a "living cesspool."

(5) Ehret says, "If you have eaten wrong for 30, 40, 50 years, thereby producing your disease, you must do the necessary compensation as reparation for your sins; you must do the opposite by eating clean, natural, divine food, which will produce health instead of disease."

iii) It was not the intention of the Creator to produce disease. It is merely the consequence of humans disobeying divine natural laws.

(1) There would have been, and would be, no disease if humans lived according to the diet offered in Genesis 1:29.

Glossary: Lesson X

Christian Science: The beliefs and practices of the Church of Christ, Scientist, a Christian sect founded by Mary Baker Eddy in 1879. Members believe that only God and the mind possess the ultimate reality, and that sin and illness are illusions, which can be overcome by prayer and faith.

Genesis 1:29 (Bible): The voice of God tells Adam and Eve that their diet should consist of fruit. Although there are many different translations of the verse, they all have a similar meaning that suggests the first humans were at best fruitarians, or, at worst, raw and mucusless fruit and vegetable eaters. One common variation is from the Vulgate, which is a late fourth-century Latin translation of the Bible: "And God said, Behold, I have given you every herb [plant] bearing seed, which is upon the face of all the earth, and every tree, in which is the fruit of a tree yielding seed: to you it shall be for food [meat]" (Vulgate translation). According to this verse, the fruit of a tree yielding seed, as well as the seeded fruit from herbs (plants such as a grapevine), are to be the food of humans.

Dietetics: The branch of knowledge concerned with the diet and its effects on health. Ehret often uses it to mean the practical application of diet for the maintenance of health and healing of illness.

Review Questions: Lesson X

1. What are the two main categories that Ehret divides all healing practices into?

2. According to Ehret, why do symptoms of illness often return after medical treatments?

3. List three physical treatments.

4. What is Ehret's opinion of exclusively using mental treatments?

Lesson XI
Confusion in Dietetics

Summary: Lesson XI

In Lesson XI, Arnold Ehret endeavors to convince the reader that 1) food is the primary cause of disease, 2) any attempt to heal will fail as long as a mucus-free diet is not adhered to, 3) that there are two main categories of food including mucus-free healing ones and mucus-forming disease-producing ones, and 5) that all other dietetic approaches fail because they stress food values while ignoring the cleansing properties of food. Ehret also expounds on his statement that "life is a tragedy of nutrition," insisting that the ignorance about what humans should eat is the "missing link" to the human mind. He concludes by stressing how important it is to understand the "system" of the Mucusless Diet Healing System, and that it is not enough to only know what foods are and are not mucusless.

Outline: Lesson XI

1) Food's Influence on Disease

   a) Food is 99.99% the cause of disease.

   b) All attempts to heal will fail so long as the importance of diet is not the primary focus.

   c) The "mucusless diet" (mucus-free foods) and "mucus-forming foods" divide all human foods into two categories:

      i) Natural and healing vs. harmful and disease-producing.

   d) All other dietetics is mainly wrong because it stresses food values (nutritional concepts) regardless of the mucus/pus content of the food, while ignoring the cleaning properties of food.

2) "Life is a Tragedy of Nutrition."

   a) The confusion and ignorance about what to eat are so great that they must be called the "missing link" of the human mind.

   b) Animals instinctively fast when sick.

      i) This is Nature's demonstration that health and disease depend mainly on eating or not eating.

   c) The average person and doctors blame everything on earth, except food and diet.

      i) Disease is as yet a mystery to most people. They do not realize how unclean the inside of the body is.

      ii) If a so-called healthy person fasts for several days, their breath and entire body discharges a foul odor, showing their system is clogged with putrid waste.

   d) Ehret again emphasizes how wrong it is to try and stop Nature's healing through drugs and serums.

   e) If food is chiefly responsible for disease, then it is self-evident that healing must be done through diet, and the most rational diet—fasting (oxygen).

   f) If any diet shall heal, it must consist not of "nourishing foods" but cleansing foods.

3) Importance of the "System"

   a) It is not sufficient to just know which foods are mucusless and which are mucus-forming. The following must be considered:

      i) How far and how fast the change can successfully be made.

      ii) How foods should be combined.

      iii) How long and often fasting must be introduced and combined during the healing diet if necessary.

   b) This is the "System" of the Mucusless Diet and Fasting that must be studied and learned.

Glossary: Lesson XI

"Tragedy of nutrition": Historically, the word tragedy initially referred to a play or other serious literary work with an unhappy ending. Later, it also came to be used to identify any unhappy event or disaster. As evidenced by Ehret's rejection of nutritional concepts, it seems that the "tragedy of nutrition" is not about the lack, or poor choice of, nutritious foods. One way to view it is that the tragedy is that the concept of nutrition 1) erroneously exists and 2) is dietetically opposed to the truth of natural laws governing animal life on earth. In other words, the tragedy is not only that people eat poorly and die, but think that they are eating healthy, or taking drugs responsibly, and die not realizing that pus- and mucus-forming foods and drugs are the foundation of their demise.

System: A set of specific methods, routines, and procedures formed to carry out a particular activity, perform a duty, or resolve a problem. It may also be defined as a purposeful, organized structure that comprises interrelated and interdependent elements that persistently impact one another (directly or indirectly) to retain their activity and the existence of the system, to achieve the intended goal of the system.

Review Questions: Lesson XI

1. Nuts are mucus-forming. (True or False) Explain.

2. According to Ehret, the average person and doctor often blame disease on many things other than diet. (True or False)

3. Ehret divides all foods into what two categories?

4. What is "systematic" about the Mucusless Diet Healing System?

5. What did Arnold Ehret mean by the concept "Tragedy of Nutrition"?

Further Reading: Lesson XI

Ehret, Arnold. 2014. *Thus Speaketh the Stomach and The Tragedy of Nutrition.* Introduced and edited by Prof. Spira. Columbus, OH: Breathair Publishing.

Lesson XII
Confusion in Dietetics—Part 2

Summary: Lesson XII

In Lesson XII, Arnold Ehret critiques several dietary philosophies and practices. First, he explains that a vegetarian's diet can be worse than that of a moderate meat-eater if they over-eat abhorrent mixtures of mucus-forming foods. He does not advocate eating meat, but merely points out that being an overeater of mostly plant-based foods is comparatively as dangerous. Ehret then critiques several doctors and healers from his era and describes the positive and negative elements of their methods. He also critiques the strict proponents of the raw-food diet, explaining that cooking does not destroy food value, i.e. nutrition, but that improper cooking destroys the potential healing properties of a food item. He explains that raw fruits and green-leaf vegetables form the mucusless diet. The mucusless diet as a healing system, however, includes raw and cooked foods to systematically and safely control one's elimination.

Outline: Lesson XII

1) Vegetarianism

    a) The average vegetarian diet only omits meat.

        i) The mixture of larger quantities of fruits (good foods) with eggs and milk cause overeating.

            (1) Vegetarianism is worse than moderate meat eating and a less mixed diet in most cases.

    b) Ehret explains that most other dietitians of his day think that sick and weak people automatically require "good, nourishing food" to be healed.

        i) Overlooking that Nature alone heals, and does so by fasting.

2) The Confusion of Ehret's Contemporaries

    a) Dr. Lahmann cited carbonic acid as the cause of disease.

        i) He failed to understand the deeper cause—fermentation caused by mucus-forming foods mixed with fruit.

        ii) He fell victim to the protein theory.

    b) Dr. Haig created the "Anti-uric-acid Diet," which shows some improvement, but still failed.

    c) Dr. Catani developed a diet of fruits, green vegetables, and meat—eliminating starch.

        i) This healed some illnesses.

        ii) The key was the laxative effect of the diet, but it did not heal perfectly.

    d) Dr. Graham's "Physiology of Nourishment" was influential at the time.

        i) He improved bread, not because whole wheat, bran, or graham is more nutritious than white bread, but because it eliminates more efficiently.

            (1) White flour makes a good paste, whereas graham and other wheat flours do not.

    e) Dr. Densmore challenged Graham, asserting that overeating cereals caused inflammation of the intestines.

        i) He advocated for more fruits and vegetables.

    f) Dr. Lahmann, Julius Hensel, and others may be considered the founders of the "mineral salt" movement.

        i) With this approach, the stress is placed on the fact that all acid- and mucus-forming foods lack mineral salts.

        ii) It proved to be a fad, like that of protein, trying to heal by overflowing the body with artificially manufactured mineral-salts while keeping up the same bad eating habits.

3) Raw-Food Diet

    a) Ehret explains that at present, the "raw-food diet" is in fashion.

        i) It represents great progress, but people think it is good for the wrong reasons.

(1) This leads to "fanatic extremes."

b) Raw foodists claim that cooking destroys food value (nutrition).

    i) Ehret argues, "Wrong cooking destroys HEALING value qualities (efficiency) of foods and can even cause them to become acid-forming."

    ii) The raw foodist hits on the same wrong stress: food value (nutrition).

c) The benefit of raw food is the rough fiber of uncooked vegetables, which relieves constipation.

    i) Ehret does not believe that body assimilates "food value" raw vegetables

d) Ehret's Lemon Experiment

    i) Put a lemon in a moderate dry heat for a few minutes. It then becomes sweet like an orange.

        (1) This is because fruit sugar is developed due to the moderate heat.

            (a) However, if it is heated too long or hot, it becomes acidic (not sweet).

    ii) On the same principle, all starchy vegetables improve when baked, as the starch is developed toward grape-sugar.

        (1) This is true of carrots, beets, turnips, cauliflower, etc.

e) Ehret explains "Raw fruits, and if desired, raw green-leaf vegetables, form the ideal food for humans. That is the mucusless diet. But the mucusless diet as a healing system uses raw, rough vegetables for their cleansing qualities; baked ones as food; and baked and stewed fruits AS A LESS AGGRESSIVE DISSOLVER of poisons and mucus to MODERATE THE ELIMINATION IN SEVERE CASES."

    i) This is one of the most important principles of the system, a point that "raw-food fanatics" ignore entirely, according to Ehret.

4) Fletcherism

a) Horace Fletcher developed a complete dietetic healing system by instructing his patients to chew every bite for 10 to 15 minutes.

    i) Ehret explains that this is a "camouflaged fast," insofar as the well-chewed food allows the digestive system to have a rest and the vital organs recuperate.

    ii) However, when continued too long, the bowels constipate from lack of solid food.

        (1) It was said that Fletcher himself died as a result of "trouble" in these organs.

b) Another camouflaged fast is any diet where you eat one item a day.

    i) An example is the "Salisbury Cure," which consisted of one piece of beefsteak and toast per day.

        (1) Never allows the body to perfectly heal.

c) The "milk diet" is also a camouflaged fast (drinking only milk).

i) The secret is if someone replaces 3 meals a day with several quarts of milk (liquid), the obstruction in the body from the milk's residue is less.

(1) But the patient will suffer eventually due to the sticky, constipating nature of milk.

5) Schroth Cure

a) Consists of eating three days of nothing but dry bread, with nothing to drink.

b) On the fourth day, an unlimited drink of light wine and some food, combined with all-night wet packs.

c) This causes a tremendous elimination, if you can stand the severity of the cure.

i) This so-called "dry cure" is also a camouflaged fast.

d) Ehret treated many people who had gone through this cure at his sanitarium, and found they had weak hearts and lacked the elastic efficiency of their tissues.

e) Ehret used the same principles for relatively strong people:

i) 2 or 3 days of eating nothing but dried fruit.

ii) Then, one day of juicy fruits and starchless vegetables.

6) Conclusion

a) Ehret explains, "There are hundreds of other dietetic cures on the 'market,' and every once in a while one of them becomes popular.

i) "Including the long fast and 'fruit fast' up to the so-called 'scientifically prepared' mixtures of medical and non-medical dieticians."

ii) None of them perfectly heal because they do not adequately address internal filth through systematic and mucus-free means.

Glossary: Lesson XII

Vegetarian: Term that refers to a variety of dietetic modalities that include the eating of plant-based foods and certain mucus-forming foods (starches or grains and fats). Some vegetarians may or may not also choose to include certain pus-forming foods such as dairy products, eggs, or fish.

Vegan: Term coined by Donald Watson in 1944 to draw a distinction between a person who abstains from all animal products, including eggs, cheese, fish, etc., from vegetarians who avoid eating meat, but may still consume certain animal products. Once all non-plant-based items are eliminated, the mucusless diet becomes, by definition, vegan.

Fruitarian: A diet that consists completely or primarily of fruits and possibly seeds and nuts, excluding all animal products.

Raw-Foods Diet (or raw-vegan diet): The practice of consuming uncooked, unprocessed, plant-based, and often organic foods as a large percentage of one's diet. Many people mistakenly believe that Ehret's work is inherently, or only, raw foodism or fruitarianism. Although the highest levels of the mucusless diet are raw, mucus-free foods, Ehret advocates using cooked mucusless foods, and some moderately mucus-forming items, as needed during the transition diet.

Mineral: A naturally occurring, homologous inorganic solid substance possessing a clearly defined chemical composition and characteristic hardness, crystalline structure, and color.

Mineral Salts: Inorganic salts that can be ingested or absorbed by living organisms. According to Ehret, the primary benefit of mineral salts found in fruits and vegetables are their ability to help cleanse the blood/body.

Camouflaged Fast: Term that refers to any method of eating or drinking that allows one's stomach and intestines to rest in a way that mimics the break that the system is afforded during a fast. Most of these are not viewed as fasting methods, and when healing success occurs, the reason is not usually attributed to the fast-like elements.

Review Questions: Lesson XII

1. Explain why Ehret said that vegetarianism could be worse than a meat-based diet.

2. Explain Ehret's views on the "raw-food diet."

3. What is a "camouflaged fast"? Give at least one example.

4. According to Ehret, radical fruit fasts without a systematic transition are irrational and potentially dangerous. (True or False)

5. Why is milk dieting dangerous?

Lesson XIII
Confusion in Dietetics—Part 3

Summary: Lesson XIII

In Lesson XIII, Arnold Ehret rejects the idea of using mathematical and chemical formulas to determine what humans should eat. In other words, he rejects the foundation of Western nutritional theory, which is built on mathematical and chemical analysis. Ehret explains that even the best foods cannot heal or nourish a body encumbered with toxic waste materials. He observes that many patients desire to know specific and special menus to heal, similar acquiring a prescription of drugs. However, Ehret affirms that the Mucusless Diet is not a collection of menus, but a system of dietetic elimination and healing.

63

Outline: Lesson XIII

1) The Nutrition Theory

    a) Ehret states, "If human nourishment could ever be figured by mathematical and chemical formulas telling exactly what to eat, you will still be fooled by Nature—just so long as any ideal food is mixed with, and put into, this waste of mucus and acids already in the human system through years of wrong living."

    b) To the average person, raw foods, or mucus-free foods, react more or less mysteriously as long as they are mixed with their uneliminated toxic waste.

        i) Most dietitians are confused and ignorant of the fact that the average person will first become worse when put on a cleansing diet.

            (1) Sometimes developing boils, sores, etc.

            (2) Other unpleasant symptoms of elimination.

    c) People want to know what to eat and acquire special menus like a drug prescription.

        i) When the elimination sets in, they blame the cleansing foods instead of the uneliminated waste in their system, or latent illnesses.

        ii) One must put up with the temporary discomfort to go through the healing process.

        iii) "The foods agree with them, but they do not agree with the foods."

2) The Mucusless Diet is different from everything else.

        i) It is not a collection of different menus for every disease.

        ii) It dispenses with the concept of "nourishing" foods.

        iii) It is not a "food list diet," where one can simply eat anything on the list.

        iv) It is not like a medical prescription or standardized diet applicable to all cases.

        v) It IS a SYSTEM of dietetic elimination of disease matter, waste, etc., slowly from the body.

            (1) The end result could be "fruits only"—or fruits and green-leaf vegetables—THE MUCUSLESS DIET.

        vi) The diet should be personally supervised by an experienced Mucusless Diet expert.

            (1) It is a progressive method of "eating your way to health" combined with short fasts if necessary.

        vii) It is a healing process which every sick person must undergo if they desire to be healed.

        viii) Ehret explains, "Nature will do her part if we but give her half a chance. Try it out for yourself and watch for the results."

Glossary: Lesson XIII

Nutrition: (1550s) from L. *nutritionem* (nom. nutritio) "a nourishing," from *nutrire* "nourish, [to] suckle," that is to "nourish" a baby with breast milk. Words like "nurse" have the same root. In modern times, the term can mean the process of providing or obtaining the food necessary for health and growth. It also refers to the branch of science that is concerned with nutrients and nutrition, particularly in humans. Ehret is one of the greatest critics of what is accepted as standardized views on nutrition.

Review Questions: Lesson XII

1. Why do raw mucus-free foods act "mysteriously" to the average person, who ultimately blames fruit or mucus-free vegetables for their ailments?

2. It is important to stick to special menus while practicing the Mucusless Diet. (True or False) Explain.

3. Why is the Mucusless Diet Healing System not like a medical prescription?

Lesson XIV
Ragnar Berg's Table (Revisited)

Summary: Lesson XIV

In the original *Mucusless Diet* book, Arnold Ehret discusses and shares Ragnar Berg's food tables, which analyze various properties of foods that popular during the early 1900s. Berg's table separates foods into different categories and gives them figures which indicate if they are "Plus or Acid-Binding" or "Minus or Acid-Forming." Many of the foods that Ehret identifies as pus- and mucus-forming are "Minus or Acid-Forming" on Berg's table. Ehret explains that he does not endorse Berg's theories on diet and that the tables are not completely accurate. He affirms, "this list is given as a comparison only and should be studied for what it is worth." In the annotated, revised, and edited edition of the *Mucusless Diet*, Prof. Spira takes an editorial liberty and replaces the Berg tables with a list of mucus-forming and mucus-free foods based on Arnold Ehret's definitions. In the editor's note, he explains that many first-time readers often think that the Berg table is an accurate food list depicting mucus-forming versus non-mucus-forming foods. Given that a number of the food items that Ehret clearly says are mucus-forming are identified as acid-binding, and that there are a number of foods eaten in the 21st century not addressed on this list, Spira shares his list of "Acid-Forming and Acid-Binding (Mucusless) Foods."

67

Outline: Lesson XIV

1) Editor's Note by Prof. Spira on the Berg Table (*Annotated Edition*)

   a) The original Berg table can be problematic and confusing for first-time readers.

   b) Ehret's primary purpose for including it was to show that Ehret was not alone in believing that acid-forming foods were injurious to the body.

      i) The problem is that many of the items on the original table are actually very acid- and mucus-forming, although listed as "acid-binding."

      ii) Generally, all "pus- and mucus-forming" foods are ultimately "acid-forming (see *acidosis*)."

   c) Ehret tries to inform the reader to take the list with a "grain of salt," but many readers continue to think that it was a mucus-free vs. mucus-forming foods chart.

      i) This leads to much confusion.

   d) Ehret explains: "The mere fact that some foods given in the list are 'acid-binding' does not necessarily mean that I endorse their use. This list is given as a comparison only and should be studied for what it is worth. Please understand that I am not endorsing Berg's theories."

   e) For the purpose of the twenty-first-century educational edition of the *Mucusless Diet*, I took an editorial liberty to provide a clearly defined list of acid-forming (pus- and/or mucus-forming) and acid-binding (mucusless) foods, as I've come to know them.

      i) Almost all of the items from the original list are included plus many others in common use today.

      ii) This list is not a "what foods I recommend," but an objective list.

      iii) I do not recommend all items that are technically mucus-free, and certain mucus-forming items are important for the transition diet.

      iv) Pus-forming and very mucus-forming foods from the list should be avoided from the beginning if possible.

      v) Moderately or slightly mucus-forming foods can be effective during the transition.

      vi) This is not an exhaustive list.

      vii) See the *Annotated, Revised, and Edited Mucusless Diet Healing System* for the whole list.

Glossary: Lesson XIV

Acid-Forming: Foods containing a large amount of acid residue following digestion.

Acid-Binding: Foods that have the capacity to neutralize and help eliminate acid-forming/mucus-forming foods.

Pus-Forming: Foods of animal origin that degrade into a thick white, yellowish, or greenish opaque liquid produced in infected tissue, consisting of dead white blood cells, bacteria, tissue debris, and serum. According to Ehret, pus-forming foods are the worst foods that humans eat.

Very Mucus-Forming: Food items that leave behind a significant amount of mucus residue in the body. These are foods that Prof. Spira advises to eliminate from one's diet as soon as possible.

Moderately Mucus-Forming: Food items that are fairly mucus-forming, but may be used during mucus-lean phases of the "Transition Diet."

Mildly Mucus-Forming: Food items that are less harmful than moderately mucus-forming items, yet mucus-forming nonetheless. These items may be used during mucus-lean phases of the "Transition Diet."

Slightly Mucus-Forming: Foods that may leave behind a minimal amount of mucus residue if not promptly eliminated from the body.

Potentially Acid-Forming: Foods that do not leave behind mucus residues, but may or may not cause harm when ingested due to their acid-forming properties.

Processed Foods: Foods that have been treated, or prepared, by special methods, especially for the purpose of preserving them.

Acid-Forming Stimulant: Food items that cause harm when ingested due to their acid-forming properties.

Relatively Starchless and Mucusless: Foods that are, or are mostly, mucus-free.

Review Questions: Lesson XIV

1. Why did Ehret include Ragnar Berg's table in his original Mucusless Diet, although he knew it was flawed?

2. According to Prof. Spira, what is the problem with the Ragnar Berg table?

3. Are all the mucus-free items on the list recommended as good to eat? (True or False) Explain.

4. What is meant by "slightly mucus-forming"?

5. What does "potentially acid-forming" mean? Give one example.

6. What are "acid-forming stimulants"?

Lesson XV
Transition Diet—Part 1

Summary: Lesson XV

In Lesson XV, Arnold Ehret shares the first part of his "Transition Diet" process, which is a fundamental part of his overall *Healing System*. He emphasizes that chronic illness cannot simply be corrected through a long fast or radical fruit diet, but that a gradual approach should be used. Ehret defines a "mucus-lean" diet as one that still includes certain mucus-forming foods that may be used during certain periods of the "Transition Diet." He explains that the speed of elimination can be controlled and regulated through the quantity and quality of foods used. In general, mucus-forming foods slow down one's elimination, while mucus-free foods promote more rapid elimination. Ehret suggests that the non-breakfast plan, or taking in no solid food early in the day, is highly beneficial and recommended. He also explains that mucusless diet practitioners should never drink during meals since mixtures of solid food and liquid are hard for the body to digest. Finally, in the remainder of the lesson, Ehret offers menu recommendations for the first two months. Ehret does not intend this plan to strictly be used verbatim by each practitioner. With his examples, Ehret seeks to reveal the gradual and systematic nature of the transition diet as a whole. Finally, Ehret reveals the formula for his herbal intestinal broom, better known today as "Innerclean."

Outline: Lesson XV

1) Introduction

   a) Everything is perfectly performed by Nature through evolutional, progressive changes (not by catastrophes).

   b) Ehret exclaims, "Nothing is more incorrect than the mistaken idea that a decades-old chronic disease can be healed through a very long fast, or a radically extended, strict fruit diet."

      i) "Nature's mills grind slow but sure."

   c) After 20 years of experience working with thousands of the sickest people, Ehret says that a "carefully selected and progressive changing 'Transition Diet' is the best and surest way for every patient to start a cure, especially for the average mixed-eater."

   d) Mucus-Lean Diet.

      i) As long as wrong foods are partially used, Ehret calls it a "Mucus-Lean Diet."

   e) Transition.

      i) The slow change from disease-producing foods to disease-healing foods (Mucusless Diet).

   f) Speed of elimination.

      i) Depends on the quantities and qualities of food and can therefore be controlled and regulated according to the condition of the patient.

   g) Non-Breakfast Plan (Introduction).

      i) The worst eating habit is a heavy breakfast every day.

      ii) No solid food should be eaten early in the morning for the best results.

        (1) It is okay to drink something.

      iii) If you find it difficult in the beginning, you may drink again, but leave enough time before lunch so the stomach is empty.

      iv) A number of minor ailments can be healed with the Non-Breakfast Plan alone.

   h) Never drink during a meal.

      i) An important principle on the Mucusless Diet: Do not drink during a meal.

        (1) If you are used to a drink with your meal, wait until a short period after your meal before drinking.

   i) Avoid soups with meals.

      i) Soups that include solid cooked vegetables combined with liquid are hard to properly digest.

      ii) Broth would be a better option than soup with solid chunks of vegetables.

      iii) Use broth if a warm drink is desired.

2) Menus for the First 2 Weeks

   a) LUNCH:

      i)   A combination salad, consisting of raw grated carrots or coleslaw or both, half and half, and two or three spoonsful of a stewed or canned vegetable, such as green peas, string beans, or spinach.

      ii) Add to this one of the following items (whatever is in season): cucumbers, tomatoes, green onions, lettuce, or other green-leaf vegetables, celery, etc., but only a sufficient quantity for flavoring.

      iii) You may make an oil dressing according to your taste if desired, using lemon juice instead of vinegar—for flavoring purposes only.

      iv) The rest of the meal should consist of one baked or stewed vegetable such as cauliflower, beets, parsnips, turnips, squash, etc.

      v)   If you still feel as though you were hungry, you may eat a small-sized baked sweet potato or one slice of toasted bran or whole wheat bread.

          (1) Fats of any kind, including ordinary butter, are unnatural and therefore should not be eaten. However, should you crave fats, it is best to use peanut butter or some other nut butter on your bread.

      vi) The object of this menu is to supply the "broom" to provide the means for mechanically cleansing the digestive tract by quantities of raw, baked, and stewed starchless vegetables.

      vii) This may be called "Ehret's Standard Combination Salad," the "intestinal broom" spoken of so frequently and so necessary for properly eliminating the stored-up poisons now being loosened during the body's housecleaning.

   b) SUPPER:

      i)   Mix (half and half) a stewed fruit such as apple sauce, stewed dried apricots, stewed dried peaches, or stewed prunes with some cottage cheese or very ripe bananas, mashed, sweetened with brown sugar or honey to taste.

          (1) Cottage cheese is optional and should only be used for people coming from a particularly bad diet, and not for a long period of time.

          (2) The bananas would be for a less "mucused," or less acid, stomach.

3) Menus for the Second 2 Weeks

   a) LUNCH (Ehret's Standard Two-Course Meal):

      i)   First a baked apple, applesauce, or other stewed dried fruit.

      ii) After ten or fifteen minutes, a combination salad as suggested in the first menu, and bran or whole wheat bread toasted if still hungry.

      iii) Cow butter should be gradually avoided and replaced by a vegetable or nut butter during the transition.

      iv) By allowing the cooked vegetables to soak on the salad for 10 or 15 minutes, it serves the purpose of a dressing.

b) SUPPER:

   i) A baked or stewed vegetable, as suggested in the first menu, followed with a vegetable salad made of lettuce and cucumber or raw celery or a little coleslaw.

4) Menus for the Third 2 Weeks

   a) LUNCH:

      i) During the summer, this should be an exclusive fruit meal—one kind only.

      ii) In winter, a sweet dried fruit, for example, prunes, figs, raisins, or dates eaten with apples or oranges; or the dried fruits can be chewed together with a very few nuts, and then followed by the fresh fruits.

      iii) If in the beginning this fails to satisfy, wait for 10 or 15 minutes and then eat a few leaves of lettuce or a cold vegetable either cooked or raw, but just a small quantity.

   b) SUPPER:

      i) A combination salad as suggested in the first menu, followed by a baked vegetable.

5) Menus for the Fourth 2 Weeks

   a) LUNCH:

      i) Fruits as in previous menus.

   b) SUPPER:

      i) First eat fruits, either baked or stewed, or fresh, followed a little later by a cold cooked vegetable, or better still a vegetable salad.

6) If You Are Losing Weight too Fast:

   a) If you find that you are losing weight too rapidly, the elimination should be slowed down by eating bread or potatoes after the vegetables.

   b) Should you feel an intense craving in the beginning for meat—a great desire returning which you cannot resist, then eat vegetables only on that day, and NO FRUITS.

7) A Dissolved Mystery

   a) Doctors and naturopaths in general do not believe in a fruit diet because:

      i) "Whoever experiments without experience with this diet of healing, whether sick or well, loses his faith immediately, as soon as they have a crisis, becomes what he or she believes to be 'seriously ill'; that is to say, a day on which a great amount of dissolved waste, debris, mucus and other poisons are taken back into the circulation, a day of great elimination."

         (1) This causes a craving for wrong foods.

         (2) This is why it is so important for every meal of a healing nature to leave the body as soon as possible.

            (a) Being mixed with loosened and dissolved poisons can be uncomfortable.

   b) Certain foods are more laxative under certain conditions.

i) Eat the foods that you have found to be the most laxative.

ii) If you do not have a bowel movement before going to bed, help with an enema, a laxative, or both.

c) Ehret's Natural Laxative.

i) Eat a few dried prunes before the other fruits are consumed.

d) Ehret's Herbal Intestinal Broom (Innerclean Formula).

i) See the *Annotated, Revised, and Edited Mucusless Diet Healing System* for the Innerclean recipe.

ii) The herbs can be taken ground and added to a glass of water. It can also be brewed as a tea.

Glossary: Lesson XV

Mucus-Lean: Term coined by Arnold Ehret to refer to the period of one's transition when some wrong foods are partially used.

Coleslaw: Shredded cabbage without mayonnaise or dressing.

Review Questions: Lesson XV

1. Why is it not good to drink or eat chunky soups?

2. Why should drinking be avoided during meals? What should be done instead?

3. Fats of all kinds should be avoided. (True or False) Explain.

4. Why is it important for a diet of healing to be digested and eliminated from the body quickly?

5. What does Ehret mean by saying that the vegetable meal should create a "broom"?

6. What does the term "mucus-lean" mean?

7. Describe the main components of "Ehret's Standard Combination Salad."

Lesson XVI
Transition Diet—Part 2

Summary: Lesson XVI

In Lesson XVI, Arnold Ehret continues to elaborate on the principles of his "Transition Diet." He reaffirms that the governing principle of food combining is simplicity, taking into account that no animal eats combinations of different foods at the same time or drinks while eating. The use of food mixtures for Ehret is specifically designed to mechanically cleanse the gastrointestinal tract. He offers food combinations for different conditions, including one for patients with worse stomach conditions, better stomachs, a patient in "crisis," special "mucus-eliminator" recipes, etc. He offers a word about dressings for salads, explaining that it should be left to one's personal taste. He suggests using olive oil with lemon juice, among other things, and emphasizes the importance of avoiding vinegar-based dressings. For drinking purposes, Ehret recommends fresh apple juice/cider, or fresh lemonade made from lemon juice, water, and honey or brown sugar as a drink. In the "Supplement to Transition Diet Menus and Combinations," Ehret explains that the "standard menu" at his sanitarium consisted of 1) a drink in the morning, 2) one or two kinds of fruit at lunch, and 3) a vegetable meal in the evening (mucus-free or mucus-lean). Ehret concludes by offering additional mucus-lean recipes.

Outline: Lesson XVI

1) Special Transition Recipes

   a) Ehret was often asked to create some kind of diet or menu book with food combinations, mucusless recipes, and menus.

      i) He wanted to teach the principles of a natural diet (simplicity), without giving too many concrete examples.

      ii) Many animals only eat one kind of food (cows only eat grass in the wild).

      iii) According to Ehret, the most ideal and natural diet is one kind of fresh fruit that is in season.

   b) During the transition diet, Ehret uses food combinations and mixtures prepared from cooked, steamed, or baked foods for technical reasons.

2) Vegetables and Fruits

   a) The only vegetables that combine well with certain kinds of fruits are raw celery, lettuce, carrots, and beets.

   b) Generally it is best to not use more than three kinds of items with the same combination.

      i) Use one as the base or "stock."

   c) For a more "mucused" or acidic stomach, use more vegetables than fruit. In an average stomach, more fruits and fewer vegetables.

      i) For a bad stomach:

         (1) Grated or shredded firm vegetables combined with a few raisins or dried figs (see book for specific recipe).

         (2) NEVER MIX NUTS WITH WET FRUITS.

   d) Fruit acids dissolve waste and form gases.

      i) This can become harmful, so "broom" it out with vegetables as needed.

      ii) Also, use stewed fruits in the beginning as a less aggressive option.

3) A "Square" Meal Substitute

   a) Before a healing crisis, or shortly after, or to satisfy cravings for wrong foods (especially rich in fat), you may take this once in a while:

      i) Take grated coconut, mixed or eaten with applesauce, stewed prunes, or sweetened apricots.

      ii) Very ripe bananas are good when one is quite "hungry."

      iii) Other kinds of nuts or nut butter may be served once in a while, but they are too rich in protein and will produce mucus and uric acid if eaten too much.

4) Improved "Cooked" Vegetables

   a) Only one kind of cooked vegetable should be used at one meal.

      i)   It can be warm or cold, mixed with green salad and raw vegetables.

  b) When slightly starchy vegetables are slowly stewed in a little water, or carefully baked, they become sweeter.

      i)   This shows that the carbohydrates are developed toward grape sugar.

      ii)   This is an improvement, not a waste.

  c) Canned foods can be used in the winter if needed.

      i)   They can be used in locations where it is very hard to find fresh produce.

      ii)   Ehret explains, "I differ from the raw food 'fanatics,' because the food value is not important in a diet of healing. It is of more importance that the patient should and shall enjoy their change of diet during the transition, until their tastes and conditions have improved."

5) Special "Mucus-Eliminator" Recipes

  a) Raisins and figs or nuts, chewed well with raw green onions at the same time, make a good mucus-eliminator.

  b) Grated horseradish mixed with honey.

      i)   There is a surprising amount of mineral salts in horseradish.

6) Recipe for a Special Dissolver of Hardened Mucus and Uric Acid

  a) Ehret claims to have healed a woman who had been paralyzed for 6 years with the following recipe when fasting or the mucusless diet was not enough:

      i)   Use caution, as this should not be taken into a mucus-filled stomach.

      ii)   Take the juice and pulp of four lemons.

      iii) Grate and peel one lemon and mix with the juice.

      iv) Sweeten with honey, brown sugar, or fruit jelly to taste.

7) Dressings

  a) This is a question of personal taste.

  b) A good salad or olive oil with lemon juice is a simple option.

  c) A spoonful of peanut butter or nut butter dissolved in water and a little lemon juice is an option.

  d) Homemade mayonnaise that uses lemon instead of vinegar is not too harmful during the transition and can be used if you enjoy it.

      i)   The editor of the *Annotated Edition*, Prof. Spira, advises people to not use mayonnaise that contains eggs unless absolutely necessary. Today, vegetarian, egg-free mayonnaise is available, although it is hard to find without vinegar.

  e) Tomatoes cooked into a sauce.

      i)   I've found that using a sugar-free, fresh tomato sauce during transition is a more sustainable and much cleaner condiment.

8) Drinks

    a) Even if table salt is discontinued, you may still get thirsty, especially when old waste is circulating.

        i) This implies that it is preferable to discontinue table salt.

    b) A light lemonade with a little honey or brown sugar will relieve thirst better than plain water.

    c) The juice of any acid or sub-acid fruit makes a good drink.

        i) The best is sweet apple cider (fresh apple juice) if not too sweet.

            (1) Sweet apple cider is raw apple juice that has not undergone filtration to remove the coarse particles of pulp. This is not "hard" apple cider, which is alcoholic.

    d) Postum, cereal coffee, or even light genuine coffee can be used during the transition if it is your customary drink.

        i) Try warm honey-lemon water to overcome a craving for coffee or regular tea in the morning.

9) Supplement to Transition Diet Menus and Combinations

    a) Ehret's Standard Sanitarium Menu.

        i) A drink in the morning.

        ii) LUNCH: One or two kinds of fruit.

        iii) SUPPER: Vegetables, mucus-lean or mucusless.

    b) Aggressive eliminations must be individually prescribed daily menus that change according to the needs of the patient.

        i) Change = Speeding up or slowing down the elimination through diet as needed.

    c) Mucusless Diet is not a "propaganda" like vegetarianism or the raw-food movement, but a clinical "therapy of eating."

        i) The knowledge in these lessons should enable the student to begin supervising their own transitions if they do not suffer from chronic illness.

    d) The healing process takes time.

10) Mucus-Lean Recipes

    a) If a little starchy food is eaten after a meal, it can be called a Mucus-Lean Diet.

        i) Cooking will make the starchy food less harmful.

    b) Raw cereals should be roasted when used.

        i) It can be a good intestinal broom toward the beginning, but can lose that effect on your body over time.

    c) Rice is a great mucus-former because it makes the best paste.

        i) Improve it by soaking overnight in water.

            (1) The water becomes slimy and smelly.

ii) Pour off the water from the rice and either fry or bake it a little.

11) A Mucus-Lean Bread Recipe

    a) See recipe in book.

Glossary: Lesson XVI

Nut: A hard-shelled seed or dry fruit containing a detachable rind or shell and inner kernel.

Distilled Water: Water from which impurities, including dissolved salts and colloidal elements, have been removed by one or more processes of distillation.

Review Questions: Lesson XVI

1. According to Ehret, what is the most natural food for humans? Why is it not advisable to eat this way in the beginning?

2. Why are cooked foods used during the transition diet?

3. How should someone eat in the beginning of their transition if they have great amount of acidity in their stomach?

4. Why are Ehret's methods different from most "raw foodist" approaches?

5. Vinegar is an important part of the Mucusless Diet. (True or False)

6. Describe Ehret's "standard menu" in his sanitarium.

7. How can starchy foods be made less harmful through cooking?

Lesson XVII
Transition Diet
(Vegetarian Recipes Revisited)
Some Improved Recipes of Salad Dressings

Summary: Lesson XVII

Lesson XVII is somewhat of a collaboration between Arnold Ehret and his editor Fred Hirsch. First, Ehret explains that condiments are much less harmful than mucus-forming foods and shares several recipes. He elucidates principles about the transition diet, including that 1) partly cooked foods should be used at the beginning, 2) vegetables should be used generously early in the transition, 3) that vegetables work more mechanically in the body than raw or cooked fruits, and 4) as time goes on, the diet should be restricted more and more to allow the healing process to go deeper. Second, Ehret's original editor and publisher Fred Hirsch adds a note, explaining that "we feel sure that Professor Ehret would have approved and granted permission to include a few mucus-lean recipes, particularly of salads, in this edition of the *Mucusless Diet Healing System,* after being convinced as we have been that the public demand requires substitutes from the present-day acknowledged method of food preparation if they are to successfully take up the Ehret method." He then identifies seven principles of the transition diet, including 1) always eat fruit first, 2) do not drink liquids of any kind with meals, 3) fruit is the most natural food for humans, 4) mix only a few varieties of foods in one meal, 5) never eat nuts with juicy fruit, 6) strive to simplify, and 7) do not overeat. Finally, Hirsch offers a number of food combinations and recipes for the transition. It should be noted that Hirsch's portion of this lesson changed considerably from the 1924 editions to the 1994 22nd edition. For example, what is now Lesson XVII was part of Lesson XVI in the 1924 editions, which made that lesson lengthy. The editor of the annotated version, Prof. Spira, made several updates to this lesson in the 2014 edition (see Lesson XVII footnotes for more on these updates).

Outline: Lesson XVII

1) Improved Recipes for Salad Dressings

   a) Condiments are much less harmful than mucus-forming foods.

      i) It would be hard for the average mixed-eater to tolerate the transition diet at first without some condiments, particularly salt.

         (1) The taste for salt will be eliminated during the course of the diet.

   b) French dressing:

      i) Ingredients: 1 teaspoonful lemon juice, four tablespoons oil, 1/4 teaspoon honey, 1/4 teaspoon salt, and 1/4 teaspoon paprika.

      ii) Mix 1 and 1/4 tablespoons of oil with the dry ingredients; stir well. Add the honey and the lemon juice. As the dressing thickens through stirring, add the rest of the oil and a little garlic for flavor if desired.

2) Some Standard Mucusless Cooked Recipes

   a) Serbian vegetable goulash.

      i) Stew coarsely sliced white or red cabbage and sliced onions with some sliced sweet peppers in a very little water or in olive oil or vegetable fat.

         (1) Finish stewing with some sliced tomatoes and a little seasoning.

      ii) Red or white cabbage with onions baked or broiled in a little fat and tomato sauce as a gravy is an appetizing dish. The same can be done with cauliflower, carrots, Brussels sprouts, beets with the leaves, etc.

      iii) The idea is to bake as dry as possible and to afford occasionally an enjoyable harmless substitute for the chops, roasts, etc., which the practitioners have discontinued.

3) Some Special Suggestions Concerning My "Cookbook"

   a) You will notice that all menus and recipes are short.

      i) When mixtures from vegetarian or raw foods recipe books are used, the patient has trouble healing.

      ii) The ideal menu for humans is the "mono-diet" with one kind of fruit that's in season.

   b) Partly cooked food is used during the transition, with an emphasis on vegetables.

      i) This is to slow down and control the elimination.

      ii) *Vital food* is not the primary goal at first, rather the food's ability to eliminate waste.

      iii) Stewed and baked fruits are also used in the beginning for this purpose.

   c) What to do if you feel bad due to elimination:

      i) If there is too much dissolved mucus and old drugs in your circulation, slow down the elimination by not eating raw fruits or even cooked fruits. Focus on cooked or raw vegetables.

(1) Vegetables work more mechanically and are less aggressive.

   d) The diet can become more restrictive as time goes on.

4) Note by the original editor Fred Hirsch:

   a) Ehret purposely omitted recipes despite requests to promote simplicity.

   b) Hirsch feels sure that Ehret would have approved and granted permission to include some mucus-lean recipes in this edition of the Mucusless Diet.

      i) Hirsch includes recipes that he asserts will be surprisingly tasty to the skeptic.

         (1) He explains that numerous equally tasty menus can be arranged by simply changing the cooked vegetable or combination of raw vegetables.

   c) Remember the following guidelines when arranging meals:

      i) Always eat fruit first.

         (1) Wait 5 or 10 minutes before eating the vegetable course.

      ii) Do not drink liquids of any kind with the meal.

         (1) Liquids interfere with proper digestion.

         (2) When consuming liquid, at least 30 minutes should lapse before and after eating.

      iii) A human's food is fruit and herbs.

      iv) Mix but few varieties.

         (1) Fruit meals should consist of not more than two kinds of fruit in season.

         (2) Your appetite will dictate the quantity to be eaten.

      v) Never eat nuts with juicy fruits.

         (1) Dried fruits can be eaten dry with nuts.

         (2) Chew together and masticate thoroughly.

      vi) Nature's own book is simplicity.

         (1) The fewer food mixtures, the better.

         (2) Generally, three different varieties should be enough—four or five is too much.

      vii) Do not overeat.

5) Sample menus and recipes

   a) See the *Annotated, Revised, and Edited Mucusless Diet* book to view these menus and recipes.

Glossary: Lesson XVII

Protose: Meat substitute made out of wheat gluten and peanuts popular in the early 1900s. This item was heavily used in early editions of the Mucusless Diet, but was removed prior to the 13th Ehret Publishing edition from 1953.

Review Questions: Lesson XVII

1. Why should fruits be eaten first (if fruits are mixed with other foods)?

2. Why is it important to avoid drinking while eating?

3. Why is it best not to eat countless mixtures?

4. A portion of the material from this lesson in the originally published *Mucusless Diet* was not written by Arnold Ehret. What portions were added, and what is the name of the person who presumably added them?

5. Based on the salad recipes in the Mucusless Diet book, create your own combination salad. Refer back to the salad recipes in the Lesson XVII text if necessary, or come up with your own and compare it to Ehret's.

Lesson XVIII
Fasting—Part 1

Summary: Lesson XVIII

In Lesson XVIII, Arnold Ehret introduces his recommended methods for fasting. He asserts that fasting is Nature's omnipotent "remedy" for healing, although it is misunderstood and feared by medical practitioners and the average person. Ehret discourages general fasting plans that do not take into account the condition of the patient. He points out that a lack of appetite when sick is a natural message from the body to fast in order for the body to have the opportunity to heal itself. Although he does not recommend long-term fasting for others, Ehret discusses his series of government-monitored extended fasting experiments, which culminated in his 49-day fasting world record. Finally, Ehret explains his views on what happens in the body during a fast. First, the avenues of circulation contract and cause superfluous water to eliminate, and the blood becomes more concentrated. Second, the body eliminates the primary obstructions from wrong and excessive eating. Third, the kidneys filter waste, and the urine should become clouded with mucus residue. During periods of great elimination, Ehret explains that the faster may experience unpleasant symptoms, but that they disappear as soon as the relevant toxic waste has traveled through the system.

Outline: Lesson XVIII

1) What Is Fasting?

    a) Due to humankind's degeneration, living without solid and liquid food is still a problem.

        i) The process is misunderstood and not accepted by average people or medical practitioners.

        ii) Even naturopathy took time to accept fasting.

    b) Fasting is Nature's omnipotent "remedy" of healing.

    c) Some expert nature-cure advocates plan general "prescriptions" of fasting, and how to break a fast regardless of the condition of the patient.

        i) This is problematic, as the individual condition and circumstance of each faster must be taken into account.

    d) Fasting is feared and misrepresented.

        i) People think they will starve to death when they are actually being healed.

        ii) There is a difference between fasting and starvation.

2) What Does a Lack of Appetite Mean?

    a) It is natural to lose one's appetite when "sick" or going through an elimination of waste.

    b) Healing requires doing the opposite of the cause, which is eating wrong foods.

    c) The reason that long fasts have failed and continue to fail is due to the ignorance regarding what is going on in the body during a fast.

3) Ehret's Fasting World Record

    a) Ehret made four public scientific tests of fasting monitored by Swiss officials.

        i) 21, 24, 32, and then 49 days.

            (1) 49 days was the fasting world record for decades.

4) What happens to the body during a fast?

    a) As soon as eating is ceased, the avenues of circulation contract, blood becomes more concentrated, and superfluous water is eliminated.

    b) The body first eliminates the primary obstructions of wrong and too much eating.

        i) This goes on for the first few days.

            (1) The patient might feel fine, but as the obstruction of circulation becomes greater, friction increases, and unpleasant symptoms may arise.

            (2) The circulation is fighting against sticky mucus, pressed out and dissolved from the inside walls.

            (3) Kidneys start to filter waste, and the urine starts to become clouded with mucus and waste materials.

ii) Once the waste is eliminated, the patient feels fine.

c) A faster can actually feel stronger many days into a longer fast than on the first few days.

  i) This is proof that vitality does not depend primarily on food.

    (1) Recall Ehret's equation Vitality = Power − Obstruction (V = P − O).

d) A friend of Ehret's and one of his first fasters walked 45 miles in the mountains on his 24th day of a fast.

e) If you drink only water during a fast, the human mechanism cleanses itself, the same as if you were to press out a dirty sponge.

  i) In this case the dirt is sticky mucus, pus, and drugs, which must pass through the circulation until thoroughly dissolved and sent through the "physiological sieve" called the kidneys.

Glossary: Lesson XVIII

Degenerate: Term that refers to the loss of physical, mental, or moral qualities considered normal and desirable.

Contraction: The process of becoming smaller, drawn together, or reduced in compass.

Review Questions: Lesson XVIII

1. Why do humans and many animals lose their appetites when sick?

2. Why do people blame weakness on the lack of food?

3. Why does a faster's urine often turn cloudy?

4. According to Ehret, fasting is a mechanical process whereby the tissue system contracts and presses out waste. (True or False)

5. Why is fasting initially a "negative proposition"?

Lesson XIX
Fasting—Part 2

Summary: Lesson XIX

In Lesson XIX, Arnold Ehret continues his discussion of fasting. First, he explains the concept of fasting cycles, explaining that every two or three days the body will loosen waste, circulate it to the kidneys, and eliminate it. Second, Ehret discusses the dangers of fasting for too long. He explains that if a person is too encumbered with toxic waste, a long fast can become dangerous since the body is too obstructed to eliminate the waste on its own. He reveals that he provided his fasters with homemade lemonade made with lemon juice, water, and honey or brown sugar, to help loosen the mucus in the circulation. Third, Ehret explains that the length of a fast cannot be determined prior to the fast, but must be the result of noting the changing conditions of the patient. He affirms that a fast should be broken as soon as the recently loosened obstructions become too great in the circulation. Fourth, Ehret offers general principles for fasting, including 1) practice a mucusless diet with enemas before the fast, 2) be careful if the patient used prescription or illegal drugs, 3) do not try to fast until the tongue is clean, and 4) every healing period can start with a 2- or 3-day fast. Finally, Ehret discusses how to break a fast. He affirms that it is important to break a fast with the right foods, and offers two case studies of people who failed to break their fasts properly. In the first study, a patient with diabetes fasted for one week and broke it with dates. Ehret says that the proper method would have been for the faster to irrigate their colon and then break the fast with raw and cooked starchless vegetables and a piece of rough bran bread. In the second case, a man over 60 did a 28-day fast and broke it with boiled vegetarian foods. Ehret affirms that this was too long and explains that hot compresses on the abdomen and high enemas might have helped, as well as starchless, mostly raw vegetables with no fruit for a while. Ultimately the two studies show how different fasting advice may be from one patient to another.

Outline: Lesson XIX

1) Fasting Cycles

   a) As long as the waste is in their circulation, the faster feels miserable.

   b) Once the waste is filtered through the kidneys, they feel better.

   c) Two or three days later, the process repeats itself.

      i) This is why conditions can change so often during a fast, and why you might feel better on Day 20 than Day 3.

2) Dangers of Too Long a Fast

   a) A long fast may be a crime if the sick organism is too greatly clogged up by waste.

   b) Fasters who died from too long a fast did not die from lack of food.

      i) Instead, they suffocated in their own waste!

      ii) It was not that they were not getting enough nutrition, but that they had too much "obstruction" or waste in their system preventing the blood from getting oxygen.

   c) Ehret gave his fasters lemonade made with a trace of honey or brown sugar for loosening and thinning the mucus in the circulation.

      i) Lemon juice and fruit acids of all kinds neutralize the stickiness of mucus and pus.

   d) If a patient has taken drugs over their entire life, their condition might become serious or even dangerous when the poisons enter into the circulation for elimination.

      i) Heart palpitations, headaches, and nervousness may set in, as well as insomnia.

         (1) These symptoms are often blamed on the "fast" instead of drugs taken years ago.

         (2) Ehret saw patients eliminate drugs they had taken 40 years before.

3) How Long Should One Fast?

   a) Nature answers this in the animal kingdom with certain cruelty: "fast until you are either healed or dead!"

      i) Ehret believes that 50 to 60 percent of "healthy" people, and 80 to 90 percent of seriously ill ones, would die from their latent diseases through too long of a fast.

   b) How long to fast cannot be determined in advance, even when the condition of the patient is known.

   c) When and how to break the fast is determined by noting:

      i) How conditions change during the fast.

   d) The fast should be broken as soon as you notice that obstructions are becoming too great and the "blood needs **new vital substances** to resist and neutralize the poisons."

   e) Ehret recommends rejecting the idea that "the longer you fast, the better the cure."

      i) Humans are the sickest animals on earth.

(1) No other animal has violated Natural laws as badly or eats as wrongly.

4) Ehret's General Principles of Fasting

   a) Prepare for an easier fast by gradually changing the diet toward a mucusless diet, and with natural laxatives and enemas.

   b) Change shorter fasts periodically with some eating days of cleansing diet (mucus-free or mucus-lean periods).

      i) In modern times, some people refer to this kind of process as "intermittent fasting."

   c) Be particularly careful if the patient used a lot of drugs.

      i) In this case a long, slowly changing preparative diet is advisable.

   d) Do not try to fast until the tongue is clean.

      i) This advice has caused trouble with what Ehret calls "fanatical fasters."

   e) In spite of the above, every cure can start with a 2- or 3-day fast.

      i) Almost every patient can do this without any harm, regardless of how serious their illness.

      ii) First a light laxative and then a daily enema make it easier and harmless.

5) How to Break a Fast

   a) The right food after a fast is very important.

      i) This also depends on the condition of the patient.

   b) Case Studies:

      i) A one-sided meat eater suffering from diabetes broke his week-long fast with dates and died from the effects.

         (1) What happened?

            (a) Terrible poisons loosened in the stomach of the one-sided meat eater during his fast, when mixed with the concentrated fruit sugar of the dates.

               (i) This caused fermentation with carbonic acid gases and other poisons that the patient could not stand the shock of.

         (2) The correct advice would have been:

            (a) First a laxative, then later raw and cooked starchless vegetables, a piece of rough bran bread/toast. Sauerkraut is also recommended in such cases.

            (b) No fruit should be eaten for a long time after the fast has been broken.

            (c) The patient should have been prepared for the fast by a longer transition diet.

      ii) A man over 60 years of age fasted 28 days (too long), and his first meal was vegetarian foods including boiled potatoes.

         (1) An operation showed that the potatoes were glued in place inside the contracted intestines by thick mucus so strong that a piece had to be cut off.

(2) This patient fasted entirely too long for a person of his age and without proper preparation.

   (a) Hot compresses on the abdomen and high enemas might have helped the elimination, along with strong eliminative laxative and starchless, mostly raw, vegetables.

   (b) No fruits for a considerable time.

iii) Given these two case studies, you can see how individually different the advice must be and how wrong it is to give general suggestions concerning how to break a fast.

Glossary: Lesson XIX

Enema: Injection of liquid into the rectum through the anus for the purpose of cleansing and evacuating the bowels.

High Enema: An enema in which the injected material reaches high into the colon.

Low Enema: An enema in which the injected material goes no higher than the rectum.

Intermittent Fasting: An umbrella term for various fasting and dietary approaches that cycle between phases of fasting and non-fasting.

Review Questions: Lesson XIX

1. How long should a person fast?

2. Does Ehret recommend long-term fasting? Why or why not?

3. What symptoms may be experienced during a fast if drugs were ever taken by, or administered to, the patient?

4. Describe Ehret's guidelines for fasting.

5. Recall the two fasting case studies that Ehret shared in Lesson XIX. Describe one of them, and explain what Ehret said they should have done to avoid the fatal mistakes made.

Lesson XX
Fasting—Part 3

Outline: Lesson XX

In Lesson XX, Arnold Ehret offers two sets of rules for fasting. Following a fast, Ehret affirms that 1) the first meals following a fast should be laxative in nature; 2) the sooner the meal passes through the system, the better; 3) an enema should be used if no good bowel movement is had within several hours; 4) the longer the fast, the more efficiently the bowels should perform; 5) the best laxative foods are fresh fruits; 6) for an average case, the fast should be broken with raw and cooked mucus-free vegetables; 7) the patient can eat as much as they like to promote a good bowel movement; and 8) if the fast is broken with fruit but there is no bowel movement, eat more fruit or a vegetable meal until a movement is achieved. Subsequently, Ehret offers a number of rules to consider during a fast, including 1) clean the lower intestine with enemas as often as necessary; 2) take a natural laxative before a longer fast; 3) if possible, remain in the fresh air; 4) only do exercise or physical work on days when the patient feels strong enough to do so; and 5) on days when the patient feels weak, sleep is restless, and doubt is entering the patient's mind, they should read through the fasting chapters and remember that they are on Nature's operating table. Ehret also shares his thoughts on fasting beverages. He criticizes "fanatics" who demand their patients only drink water, and recommends a light lemonade or fruit juice be used. For a longer fast, he recommends making broth from cooked vegetables. He also discusses his non-breakfast plan, which is the practice of abstaining from eating solid foods early in the day. Finally, he points out that eating stops or slows down the body's process of elimination, causing the faster to potentially feel better for a period of time. Ehret suggests that this might be why overeating became such a prevalent habit.

Outline: Lesson XX

1) Important Rules to Be Carefully Studied and Memorized

    a) The first meal and menus for a few days following a fast must be of laxative effect.

        i) Not "nourishing" foods as most people think.

    b) The sooner the first meal passes through the body, the more efficiently it carries out the loosened mucus and poisons from the intestines and stomach.

    c) If no good natural bowel movement is had after two or three hours, help with natural laxatives and enemas.

        i) Ehret Testimonial:

           (1) Ehret usually had a good bowel movement at least one hour after eating.

           (2) After breaking a long fast, Ehret spent a lot of time on the toilet the following night.

    d) The longer the fast, the more efficiently the bowels perform at the end.

        i) Provided that the patient was ready and advised to do a long fast.

    e) The best laxative foods are fresh fruits.

        i) Especially cherries and grapes.

        ii) Soaked or stewed prunes are good too.

        iii) Fruits should not be used after a meat-eater's first fast, but only those who have transitioned for a while.

    f) In the average case, the fast should be broken with raw and cooked starchless vegetables.

        i) Stewed spinach is particularly good.

    g) If the first meal does not cause any unpleasantness, the patient should eat as much as they like.

        i) Eating only a small amount of food for the first 2 to 3 days without experiencing a bowel movement—owing to the small amount of food eaten—is dangerous.

    h) If you do break a fast with fruit and have no bowel movement after an hour, eat more fruit or a vegetable meal as suggested above.

        i) Eat until you have a bowel movement and bring out the accumulated waste materials.

2) Rules during the Fast

    a) Clean the lower intestines with enemas as well as you can.

        i) Do this at least every other day.

    b) Before a longer fast, take a laxative occasionally, especially before the beginning of the fast.

    c) If possible, remain in the fresh air day and night.

    d) Take a walk, exercise, or do some physical work only when you feel strong enough to do it.

        i) If tired and weak, rest and sleep as much as you can.

e) On days you feel weak, sleep may be restless, and you may have bad dreams.

   i) This may be caused when poisons pass through your brain.

   ii) Ehret explains: "Doubt, loss of faith, will arise in your mind; then take this lesson and read it over: and over, as well as the other fasting chapters and especially Lesson V. Don't forget that you are parenthetically speaking, lying on Nature's operating table; the most wonderful of all operations that could be performed; and without the use of a knife! If any extraordinary sensation occurs due to the drugs that are now in the circulation, take an enema at once, lie down, and if necessary break the fast, but not with fruits."

   iii) Whenever you arise after lying down, do it slowly, or you may become dizzy.

3) Fasting Drinks

   a) The "fanatic" fasting enthusiast drinks only water.

   b) Ehret considers a light lemonade with honey or brown sugar or a little fruit juice to be best.

   c) Drink as much as you want during the day, but not more than two or three quarts per day.

      i) The less you drink, the more aggressively the fast works.

   d) As a change, vegetable broth from cooked starchless vegetables is good during a longer fast.

   e) Be careful when using acid-fruits during longer fasts.

      i) Poisons may be released too quickly.

4) Morning Fast or Non-Breakfast Plan

   a) The worst of all eating habits is the heavy breakfast.

   b) The only time humans do not eat for 10 to 12 hours is during periods of sleep.

   c) As soon as the stomach is free from food, the body starts the process of elimination.

   d) Avoid eating in the morning (skip breakfast).

5) Another "Mystery" Revealed

   a) As soon as you refill the stomach with food, THE ELIMINATION STOPS.

      i) The patient then feels better.

   b) This is presumably why eating unnaturally became a habit.

   c) Ehret says, "The more waste humans accumulate, the more they must eat to stop the elimination."

Glossary: Lesson XX

Breakfast: Mid-15c., from *break* (v.) + *fast* (n.). Refers to a meal eaten after a period of fasting, or a meal that ends the period of fasting during sleep.

Non-Breakfast Plan: Ehret's recommendation to take no solid food before lunchtime. Drinks can be used.

Review Questions: Lesson XX

1. A fast should be broken with a meal that is laxative. (True or False) Explain.

2. If a bowel movement is not had after a fast is broken, what should be done?

3. What is meant by "Nature's operating table"?

4. How much juice or lemonade may be consumed during a fasting day?

5. Why is a heavy breakfast so bad?

6. List two of Ehret's six rules to remember during fasting periods.

Lesson XXI
Fasting—Part 4

Summary: Lesson XXI

In Lesson XXI, Arnold Ehret concludes his discussion of fasting methodology. First, he explains that the 24-hour fast, or one-meal-a-day plan can be a preliminary step toward a longer period of fasting to heal severe cases. If fruits and vegetables are eaten in the same meal, the fruits should be eaten first, followed by the vegetables 15 to 20 minutes later. Second, Ehret discusses fasting as a tool of the *Mucusless Diet Healing System*. Ehret affirms that he is no longer in favor of long fasts and that short-term fasting, 24 hours or 3 to 5 days, is safer. He suggests that patients start with short fasting periods and gradually work toward longer ones as needed. Third, Ehret emphasizes that it is insane to give a sick person food. Finally, Ehret offers philosophical thoughts on what he calls the "Superior Fast." He references how skinny Indian fakirs are, but how they are some of the best fasters in the world. Ehret explains that the cleaner a person is, the easier it is for them to fast. He says that if "you simply supply the 'engine' with the necessary water that is used up, you ascend into a higher state of physical, mental, and spiritual condition. I call this the 'Superior Fast.'" Ehret concludes by sharing his philosophy that the practice of fasting, and not volumes of psychology or philosophy, is the key for a person to lead a superior life and perceive divine revelations within the physical and spiritual worlds.

Outline: Lesson XXI

1) The 24-Hour Fast, or One-Meal-a-Day Plan

    a) The patient can heal more severe cases with the 24-hour fast.

        i) This can be a preliminary step to longer fasts if chronically encumbered.

    b) The best time to eat is in the afternoon, around 3 or 4 pm.

    c) Fruits should be eaten first, and then after 15 or 20 minutes, the vegetables.

        i) All should be eaten within an hour.

2) Fasting When Used in Connection with the *Mucusless Diet Healing System*

    a) Ehret is no longer in favor of long fasts.

        i) He explains that it may be criminal to let a patient fast for 30 or 40 days on water.

            (1) Contracting the avenues of circulation with old waste.

    b) If fasting is going to be used:

        i) Start with the non-breakfast plan.

        ii) Then follow the 24-hour fast for a while.

        iii) Gradually increase up to 3- to 5-day fasts.

        iv) Ehret explains that the blood is gradually improved and waste eliminated through this kind of intermittent fasting.

        v) This is the *Mucusless Diet Healing System* with "fasting" as an important part of it.

3) Fasting in the Cases of Acute Disease

    a) It is insanity to give food to a sick person.

        i) For instance, someone with pneumonia and a high fever should fast.

    b) Ehret explains, "Air baths taken in the room, enemas, natural laxatives, and cool lemonade would save the lives of thousands of young men and women who are now daily permitted to die, the innocent victims of pneumonia or other acute diseases—due to the stubborn ignorance of doctors and so-called highly civilized people."

4) The Superior Fast

    a) Ehret says that the Indian "fakir" is the greatest faster in the world today.

        i) They are usually nothing but skin and bones.

        ii) This shows that the cleaner a person is, the easier it is for them to fast.

    b) The elasticity of the entire tissue system is improved through fasting.

    c) The body does not have to work as hard when there is less obstruction.

    d) Ehret says "And if you simply supply the 'engine' with the necessary water that is used up, you ascend into a higher state of physical, mental, and spiritual condition. I call this the 'Superior Fast.'"

e) Ehret explains that your brain will function in an incredible manner when your blood is cleansed through fasting.

  i) The faster will feel a slight electric current.

f) Ehret asserts that, "You will learn and realize that fasting and superior fasting (and not volumes of psychology and philosophy) is the real and only key to a superior life, to the revelation of a superior world, and to the spiritual world."

Glossary: Lesson XXI

Air Bath: A hygienic exposure of the body to the open air.

Fakir: A "fakir" is an ascetic mendicant or holy person, especially one who performs feats of endurance, rejects worldly pleasures, and lives solely on alms. They are known for their ability to fast for long periods of time.

Superior Fast: See note #96 in the *Annotated, Revised, and Edited Mucusless Diet Healing System* for an extended discussion about what Ehret means by "superior fast."

Review Questions: Lesson XXI

1. What is a "24-hour fast"?

2. How should the length of one's fast be increased?

3. What is meant by the "Superior Fast"?

4. What does Ehret claim will happen to your thoughts and aspirations after the cleansing of your body?

Lesson XXII
Destructive Diet of Civilization and the Mucusless Diet, the Natural Food of Humans

Summary: Lesson XXII

In Lesson XXII, Arnold Ehret shares his thoughts on what he calls the "Destructive Diet of Civilization" and the "Natural Food of Humans," namely the Mucusless Diet. He explains that it is ridiculous to analyze "food values," in other words nutritional values. It is, instead, important to abstain from unnatural foods that clog up the body. He identifies meat, eggs, milk, fats, cereals, legumes, potatoes, rice, and nuts as mucus-forming and not part of a natural human diet. Although some foods that fall into these categories are recommended to be used as transitional tools, such as well-toasted 100% grain bread, Ehret affirms that all of these foods are unnatural for humans. Ehret concludes that what civilized people find appetizing is absurd and the result of the destructive diet of civilization.

Outline: Lesson XXII

1) The Natural Food of Humans

    a) Arnold Ehret asserts, "The wonder is that we live in spite of our excessive eating, in spite of our eating such wrong, destructive foods."

        i) Ehret asserts that it is ridiculous to note the "endless fight and confusion regarding dietetics, protein, mineral salts, vitamins, etc. The potential food value is not the first question at all."

    b) You cannot heal drunkenness by water without stopping the intake of alcohol.

        i) You cannot heal disease without stopping the eating of disease-producing foods.

    c) Ehret names the natural food of humans to be:

        i) Fruits and herbs/green-leaf vegetables (mucusless diet).

    d) Ehret explains that the "trash" of scientific dietetics is useless and in vain so long as the following is not understood:

        i) How much waste a food item produces and leaves behind in the body.

        ii) The dissolving, eliminating, healing properties.

2) Destructive Foods with No Positive Food Value

    a) Meats.

        i) Meat is in a state of decomposition.

        ii) Producing cadaver poisons and creating uric acid in the body.

        iii) Fats are the worst.

            (1) Butter is unusable in the body.

            (2) No animals eat isolated fat.

    b) Eggs.

        i) Eggs are even worse than meats.

            (1) Not only do they have protein qualities that are much too high, they contain a gluey property much worse than meat.

        ii) They are very constipating.

        iii) Hard-boiled eggs are less harmful, because the gluey quality is destroyed

        iv) Egg whites make a perfect glue.

    c) Milk.

        i) Also makes good glue for painting.

        ii) Cow's milk is too rich for adults and babies and destructive.

            (1) A human baby's stomach cannot digest what a calf can.

iii) Sour milk and buttermilk are less harmful and possess some laxative qualities.

    (1) Cottage cheese with stewed fruit can be used for transitional purposes if needed.

    (2) All other kinds of cheese should be avoided.

d) Fats.

  i) Ehret asserts that, "All fats are acid forming, even those of vegetable origin, and are not used by the body."

  ii) You will only like and crave them if you are congested with waste.

e) Cereals.

  i) Cereals and all flour products are mucus- and acid-forming.

  ii) Bran, graham, whole wheat, or rye bread is less harmful, as their ingredients have lost some of their stickiest qualities.

    (1) When well done or toasted and well baked, they are much less harmful.

  iii) Raw cereals, if toasted, can to some extent act as a mucus-broom.

f) Legumes.

  i) Lentils, dried beans, and dried peas are too rich in protein, similar to meat and eggs.

  ii) The peanut is also a legume.

g) Potatoes.

  i) They are a little better than flour products because they have more mineral salts.

    (1) They do not make a good paste.

  ii) Well fried or crusty, baked like Saratoga chips, sweet potatoes are almost mucusless.

h) Rice.

  i) One of the greatest mucus formers.

    (1) It makes an excellent glue (used for book-binding).

  ii) Ehret believes, through his observations, that rice is the foundational cause of leprosy.

i) Nuts.

  i) All nuts are too rich in protein and fat.

    (1) They should only be eaten in the winter time and/or sparingly.

    (2) Nuts should be chewed together with some dried sweet fruits or honey.

      (a) Never with juicy fruits, because water and fat do not mix.

j) Summary.

  i) With the exception of nuts, all the above-mentioned foods need to be prepared in some way to be eaten.

  ii) What civilized people call tasty is absurd.

(1) If the tongue is clean from mucus, as well as the nose, they both become "magic mirrors" (revelation organs).

(2) A person loses the desire for stimulating spices after having cleansed enough.

(3) The sense organs of humans are generally in a pathological state, embodied in pus-like mucus and waste.

    (a) Being in a partly decayed condition themselves is why they find this half-rotten food palatable.

iii) Culinary Arts are nothing more than the "art to cover the real taste and odor by spices and dressings."

(1) Pathological people prefer the odor of rotting, dead, cooked flesh to a ripe piece of fruit.

iv) It is true that civilized people starve to death:

(1) Through overeating of wrong, destructive foods.

(2) The stomach is disfigured.

    (a) See *Thus Speaketh the Stomach* for more about the condition of the human stomachs.

v) Ehret recommends reading *Natural Food of Man* by Hereward Carrington, who shows that a natural human diet consists of fruit.

(1) Even experts on fruit diet and raw-foods have doubts that today's degenerate humans can live the paradisiacal life.

vi) All other diet experts and doctors base their work on the "old physiology."

(1) Ehret says, "All others, not knowing these new truths and not possessing the necessary knowledge contained only in the *Mucusless Diet Healing System* can never secure a perfectly clean body and complete healing as well as possess an understanding of every situation."

Glossary: Lesson XXII

Calorie: The large calorie, also called the dietary or nutritional calorie, is the amount of energy needed to raise the temperature of one kilogram of water by one degree Celsius. For an in-depth analysis of Ehret's relationship to the calorie theory, see note # 98 in the *Annotated, Revised, and Edited Mucusless Diet Healing System*.

Review Questions: Lesson XXII

1. What is Ehret's opinion of scientific dietetics, food values, and their statistics?

2. Are avocados mucus-forming? Why or why not?

3. Does Arnold Ehret recommend using hard-boiled eggs?

4. Well-baked or well-fried sweet potatoes are close to being mucusless. (True or False)

5. According to Ehret, rice is one of the greatest mucus-forming foods. (True or False)

6. Can cereals be used during the transition? If so, how should they be prepared?

7. Explain why nuts are mucus-forming. If eaten at all, how should they be eaten?

8. Why do most pus- or mucus-forming foods need to be prepared or processed in order to eat?

Further Reading: Lesson XXII

Ehret, Arnold. 2014. *Thus Speaketh the Stomach and The Tragedy of Nutrition*. Introduced and edited by Prof. Spira. Columbus, OH: Breathair Publishing.

Carrington, Hereward. 1963. *The Natural Food of Man: Being an Attempt to Prove from Comparative Anatomy, Physiology, Chemistry and Hygiene, That the Original, Best and Natural Diet of Man Is Fruit and Nuts*. Mokelumne Hill, CA: Health Research, 1963.

Lesson XXIII
Sex

Summary: Lesson XXIII

In Lesson XXIII, Arnold Ehret discusses issues related to sex and diseases of the reproductive organs. He explains that diseases of the sexual organs are relatively easy to heal through diet and fasting. He asserts that drugs and a meat-rich diet are more to blame for sexual diseases than actual intercourse. Given that mercury was used as a treatment for some venereal diseases in the early 20th century, Ehret explains that such patients must avoid a radical fruit diet or fast, and that expert supervision is necessary. On the psychology of sex, Ehret asserts that humans of civilization are the products of stimulation and not real love vibrations. In other words, the poisonous foods of civilization stimulate people to satisfy their sexual urges in an uncontrollable manner. He suggests that a mucus-free diet can allow the practitioner to regain control over their sexual urges, and asserts that the only way to heal impotence is through the diet. Ultimately, he asserts that sex, when had by people not stimulated by the destructive foods of civilization, is a natural part of life and an expression of vitality.

Outline: Lesson XXIII

1) Sex Diseases

    a) Ehret says that venereal diseases can be healed by diet and fasting fairly easily.

        i) Especially if the person is younger.

    b) Gonorrhea.

        i) Ehret characterizes it as a "cold" of the reproductive organs.

        ii) Ehret says it is easy to heal with the Mucusless Diet and fasting if the patient did not take any drugs.

        iii) It is simply "an elimination" through these organs.

            (1) One-sided meat eaters are very susceptible to the disease.

        iv) If drug injections are used for an extended period, the mucus and pus are thrown back into the prostatic gland, bladder, etc.

            (1) The entire uterus becomes inflamed for women.

        v) Ehret says he had hundreds of sexual disease cases where naturopathy failed to heal.

            (1) Only fasting and the mucus-free diet were able to help.

        vi) Ehret points out that syphilis does not exist in the animal kingdom or among uncivilized people.

            (1) He blames drugs and the diet of civilization for these diseases.

                (a) Drugs and a meat diet are far more to blame than sexual intercourse, according to Ehret.

        vii) If a patient is poisoned by mercury, a careful and long transition is needed.

            (1) A radical fruit diet or fast could become harmful if the drugs are dissolved and enter back into the bloodstream at once.

            (2) Expert supervision is required for mercury poisoning.

2) Sex Psychology

    a) The philosopher says that an "unclean person has no right to produce a new being."

        i) "You shall not only generate, but reproduce yourself," says that great thinker, Nietzsche.

    b) Humans of civilization are the products of "stimulants" instead of love vibrations.

        i) Procreation is the most holy and divine act, and the father has the highest responsibility to be clean.

            (1) If the semen/father's seed, what Ehret calls "germ," has any defect, it is a generation going backward, not forward.

        ii) In ancient civilization, sex was a "cult, a religion," and love the subject of many mythological tales.

(1) This demonstrates a conscious or unconscious goal to reproduce their kind.

c) Statistics show that every family of the city's population dies out, disappears, with the third or fourth generation.

i) The sins of the parents produce diseased children.

ii) You may "love your neighbor" but kill your own child before it's even born.

iii) "How can a defective germ grow into a perfect being between a filthy, mostly constipated colon and an unclean bladder of a civilized mother?"

d) One of the worst tragedies is a pregnant woman who eats twice as many dead "cadavers" of animals killed years ago, because she is advised to "eat for two."

3) Natural Control of Sex

a) It is a disaster to stimulate the sexual organs continually through wrong diet and believe sexual urges can be suppressed or controlled by preaching morals or philosophical doctrine.

i) Nature does not listen to you, but you must listen to Nature.

ii) Ehret explains, "We are the product of stimulations, and not of natural love vibrations, which eventually leads to impotence."

b) The only way to heal impotence is through fasting and the Mucusless Diet.

i) Sex is part of vitality and even a barometer of regeneration, youth, etc.

(1) Ehret has seen sterility of the female healed.

ii) No one in civilization knows what genuine "love vibrations" are from a cleansed body.

(1) The beard of man is a secondary sex organ.

(a) Beardless, hairless and bald makes for a second-rate sex quality.

(i) See Judges 16: 13–20.

(2) See more about what Ehret has to say about hair in *Rational Fasting*.

c) Masturbation, night emissions, prostitution, etc., may be eliminated from the sex life of someone on the Mucusless Diet after their body has become clean and powerful.

i) Ehret explains, "Love is the greatest power and it is, if natural, the highest 'invisible food' from the infinite for soul and body."

Glossary: Lesson XXIII

Sex Diseases (Sexually Transmitted Disease): Various diseases that a person can get by having sexual contact with a person who is already infected with the disease.

Sterile: The state of being incapable of producing offspring.

Judges 16:13–20: In the Hebrew Bible, Samson (meaning "man of the sun") was granted supernatural strength by God in order to combat his enemies and perform heroic feats. His two fatal flaws, however, were his attraction to deceptive women and his hair, without which he would lose his power and vitality. In these verses, Delilah is trying to discover what gives Samson his great strength so that she may find a way to subdue him. He finally admits that his hair had never been cut and that it is the source of his great strength.

Review Questions: Lesson XXIII

1. Ehret claims that sexual diseases can easily be healed through diet and fasting. (True or False)

2. Why does Ehret characterize some sex diseases as "colds" of the reproductive organs?

3. What does Ehret mean when he says that humans of civilization are products of "stimulants" and not true love vibrations?

4. What is Ehret's opinion of facial hair on men?

5. Why does Ehret claim that the Mucusless Diet and fasting are the only way to heal impotence?

Further Reading: Lesson XXIII

Ehret, Arnold, 2014. *Prof. Arnold Ehret's Rational Fasting for Physical, Mental, and Spiritual Rejuvenation: Introduced and Edited by Prof. Spira*. Columbus, OH: Breathair Publishing.

Lesson XXIV
Sex—Part 2

Summary: Lesson XXIV

In Lesson XXIV, Arnold Ehret elucidates philosophical ideas about human reproduction and the mucus-free lifestyle. First, Ehret asserts that a mother living on a mucus-free diet could produce a god-like child. Based on his research, he proposes that the negative symptoms of menstruation and menstrual cycles could be eliminated in the bodies of a mucus-free woman. He asserts, in addition, that childbirth is painless for a physiologically clean woman. However, Ehret does not advise a pregnant woman to radically change her diet, but that the diet should be improved at least several months before conception. Second, Ehret discusses feeding babies. He warns against using cow's milk and says that it should be diluted if it is used. Ehret recommends feeding the baby fresh fruit juices diluted with water as soon as possible. He points out that babies must go through the same cleansing process as adults, and that their latent illnesses must be considered. Further, he asserts that natural sweets from fruits are necessary for the child to grow properly. Third, Ehret philosophically connects the father's sperm as a plant's seed and woman's egg as the soil. He affirms that a defective seed cannot produce a healthy plant no matter how great the soil is. The inference is that it is particularly important for men to be cleansed of waste and latent illnesses before having children. Finally, Ehret points out that many "genius" artists, inventors, etc., were from parents who could not afford luxurious diets. The inference is that their meager diets, in comparison to those of rich people, ultimately allowed them to enjoy creative abilities that may have otherwise been obstructed.

Outline: Lesson XXIV

1) Motherhood and Eugenics

    a) Motherhood with a mucusless diet, before, during, and after pregnancy is the development toward the Madonna-like, holy purity principle, different from "ordinary" childbirth.

    b) If the female body is clean through this diet, menstruation or menstrual symptoms disappear.

        i) Every one of Ehret's female patients reported that their menses became less and less.

            (1) 2-, 3-, and 4-month intermission, and then finally disappearing.

    c) "Diseases" of pregnancy, like toothaches, headaches, etc., disappear.

        i) This leads to painless childbirth.

            (1) Sweet breast milk.

            (2) Babies that do not cry.

    d) Ehret explains, "It is not advisable to start a radical change in diet during pregnancy, or while nursing; this should be done at least 2 or 3 months before conception."

        i) Eating for two is not necessary if the body is clean.

        ii) Modern babies are overfed, hence the dangerous childbirth.

            (1) The only reasonable change is to increase the eating of natural sweets such as figs, raisins, dates, grapes, etc.

2) Feeding the Baby

    a) Do not use cow's milk if the mother's milk is insufficient or bad.

        i) If cow's milk is used, it must be diluted and sweetened with honey.

        ii) Start feeding the baby as soon as possible with a teaspoonful of good fresh fruit juices diluted with water.

            (1) Juice from stewed beets is also good.

        iii) Babies crave sweetness, which shows that fruit sugar is the "essence" of all dietetics.

    b) What is viewed as an average, well-fed, healthy-looking baby is in reality pounds of waste or decayed milk.

    c) A baby must go through the same cleansing, healing process as do adults.

        i) Cleansed of latent illnesses.

        ii) Ehret believes that a baby well nursed by good mother's milk (without protein supplements) will grow wonderfully.

            (1) After the weaning period, they could be raised on apples alone.

    d) Natural sweets are necessary for the child to grow a strong skeleton.

        i) Lime is also important.

    ii) Ehret says, "There is no higher moral duty of any kind than to produce a perfect being."

3) Eugenics of a Diseaseless, Superior Race

    a) Motherhood represents the soil, and fatherhood the seed.

        i) Poor soil can still produce a fairly good plant if the seed is good.

            (1) But a defective seed, even planted in good soil, will produce NOTHING.

    b) Medical doctors and naturopaths both make arguments about humanity based on filthy bodies living on an unnatural diet.

    c) Until you experience Ehret's teachings on your own body, you will have to keep an open mind.

    d) Ehret mentions that the European royal family kept their family trees clean through inbreeding only as long as they did not live in modern luxury.

        i) Noble families are disappearing because they failed to continue the generation of males.

            (1) The luxurious diet of today is to blame.

4) Predetermination of Sex/Gender

    a) Humans are what they eat.

        i) Ehret observes that many so-called "genius" artists, inventors, etc., were of poor parentage.

            (1) Thus, their diets were more meager and not as "luxurious."

    b) Ehret asserts that when diet and intercourse are restricted, there is a higher likelihood of having a male child.

        i) Ehret shares a case study of a number of young people taking refuge together in a house in Florence, Italy.

            (1) For weeks they had nothing to eat, and then only sparse amounts.

        ii) They got married and generated the family of Medici, which produced great artists, statesmen, scientists, etc.

    c) Ehret says, "when humans ascend to a God-like being, as they must have been in prehistoric times on the divine diet. The magnetic sex emanations become so wonderful that love combined with gluttony appears as a crime."

    d) Ehret continues, "Humans were once a higher, superior kind of being, not a species of the monkey family! We are only a shade of the original human, caused through our degeneration, but you may yet experience what cannot be described, that this kind of eugenics is the fundamental truth of evolution into 'Heaven on Earth!'"

Glossary: Lesson XXIV

Menstruation: The process in a woman of discharging blood, mucosal tissue, and other materials from the lining of the uterus at intervals of about one lunar month from puberty until menopause, except during pregnancy.

Eugenics: Term coined in 1883 by English scientist Francis Galton (1822–1911), is an analogy of ethics, physics, etc. from Greek *eugenes* or "well-born, of good stock, of noble race," from eu- "good" + genos "birth." The term is associated with a biosocial movement and philosophy advocating the improvement of human hereditary traits through promoting higher reproduction of more desired people and traits, and reduced reproduction of less desired people and traits. Propagators tended to believe in the genetic superiority of Nordic, Germanic, and Anglo-Saxon peoples; supported strict immigration and anti-miscegenation laws; and supported forcible sterilization of the poor, disabled, and "immoral." Ehret used the term "eugenics" to make a philosophical point about the potential for developing an improved race of humans through the *Mucusless Diet Healing System*. For many modern readers, this term is off-putting due to its historical association with racist and genocidal policies. Of course, Ehret wrote this text well before the climax of radical eugenic policies in the United States and by Hitler in Germany. Yet, Ehret's beliefs about a so-called superior race of people are diametrically opposed to the white supremacist mentality that was the foundation of most eugenic programs. (For more on this discussion, see note #103 in the *Annotated, Revised, and Edited Mucusless Diet Healing System*.)

Review Questions: Lesson XXIV

1. How did Ehret use the term "eugenics" differently than his peers? How might this confuse modern readers?

2. What did Ehret recommend future parents do?

3. What should a baby consume?

4. What is meant by the statement that "humans were once a higher, superior kind of being, not a species of the monkey family"?

Lesson XXV
The Enforcement of Elimination by Physical Adjustments: Exercises, Sunbaths, Internal Baths, and Bathing

Summary: Lesson XXV

In Lesson XXV, Arnold Ehret discusses auxiliary therapies, including exercise, sunbathing, internal baths (enemas), and external baths. First, he asserts that it can be dangerous to violently and unnaturally vibrate or shake the tissues in order to stimulate the circulation, especially through extreme exercising. Although it may help eliminate waste initially, in the long term it could damage the elasticity of the tissues. He explains that the most natural exercises are walking, dancing, and singing. Ehret then describes nine exercises that he recommends for use with the Mucusless Diet. Second, Ehret discusses the importance of sunbathing. He says to start off with 20 to 30 minutes and to keep one's head covered at first. According to Ehret, the cleaner the practitioner becomes, the more they will be able to stand, and enjoy, exposure to the hot sun on their naked body. Third, Ehret discusses "internal baths," or enemas. He says that it is advisable to use enemas throughout the transition diet and definitely during fasting periods. He recommends that the patient perform an enema following a natural bowel movement, and offers some instructions for performing an enema. Finally, Ehret discusses his thoughts on bathing. He explains that it is not necessary to take a hot bath every day, but that it is important to use water to open up the pores. For baths with water, Ehret recommends adding water to a small basin and using the hands to rub the body down with the water. He also recommends "air bathing," which consists of spending a few minutes a day in front of an open window massaging the body to help the skin retain its natural functioning qualities. Finally, Ehret asserts that extremes of all kinds should be avoided, including those related to exercise and bathing.

Outline: Lesson XXV

1) Physical treatments vibrate or shake the tissues and stimulate circulation.

    a) This can loosen and help eliminate foreign matter (the cause of disease).

        i) The body does this itself through fasting.

    b) Physical treatments and culture can therefore be combined with this diet and fasting to enforce and hasten elimination.

        i) Extreme care must be taken not to overwork oneself on days of strong elimination.

            (1) If you are tired, rest and sleep as much as possible, especially during a fast.

    c) The best and most natural exercises are walking, dancing, singing, etc.

        i) Singing is the most natural breathing exercise with the added advantage of loosening chest vibrations.

        ii) Hiking in the mountains is a great exercise.

            (1) When climbing hills, one naturally increases their breathing.

        iii) Both hands should be free when walking, to permit natural movement.

        iv) By taking proper care of your body, one will generate health.

    d) Ehret's Exercises

        i) Designed for those who want to stay physically fit.

        ii) Do not exercise in a closed, stuffy room.

        iii) Stand before a window.

        iv) Take a deep, full breath with each exercise.

        v) Inhale through the nose and exhale through the mouth.

            (1) One can also stand before a mirror and observe their graceful manner.

            (2) Ehret says, "Fall in love with yourself if no one else will."

        vi) Keep the feet about 15 inches apart—stand erect and use muscular tension.

        vii) See Lesson XXV in the *Annotated, Revised, and Edited Mucusless Diet* to see the description of Ehret's nine exercises.

            (1) Do not become exhausted with any exercise.

            (2) If one becomes stiff at first, it is a sign that the exercise was needed.

            (3) The soreness will soon wear off if one continues the daily exercise routine.

            (4) Additional exercises may be added, but be sure to maintain deep breathing.

            (5) One's favorite music can be played while exercising.

            (6) Do not view it as a duty, but put fun into them.

2) Sunbaths

a) Whenever possible, take a sunbath.

    i) In the beginning do not exceed 20 to 30 minutes and keep head covered.

    ii) On days of great elimination, stay cool.

b) The cleaner one becomes, the more enjoyable sunbathing will be.

    i) More heat can be withstood for longer periods of time.

    ii) The sunbath is an excellent "invisible" waste eliminator.

    iii) It rejuvenates the skin, causing it to become silky soft and coloring a natural brown.

    iv) All clothing should be removed.

        (1) Idea: build a small enclosure in your back yard, or on the roof, away from prying eyes.

        (2) The clothing of civilization has made it impossible for humans to secure their proper quota of fresh air and sunshine, essential to happiness.

        (3) The direct sun rays on the naked body supply the electricity, energy, and vitality for the human storage battery, renewing it in vigor, strength, and virility.

3) Internal Baths (Enemas)

a) Ehret says, "During the transition period, even though you have regular bowel movements, it is advisable to wash out the lower colon."

    i) The sticky waste and slimy mucus, etc., which Nature is attempting to eject should be helped as much as possible.

b) A small-bulb infant syringe can be used after a regular bowel movement.

    i) However, for thorough cleaning, two or three quarts of water should be used.

c) Try to have a natural bowel movement before injecting the water.

    i) The body should be in a reclining position.

    ii) The syringe should not be higher than three or four feet above the patient.

    iii) Water should be warm, not hot.

    iv) If there is any discomfort, stop the flow until it passes.

    v) The entire two or three quarts should be retained at one time.

    vi) If the cramp or pain becomes too great, allow the water to pass from the colon and repeat the operation.

    vii) The water should be retained for 15 to 20 minutes, or as long as is comfortable.

    viii) While still lying on your side, gently massage the colon in an upward motion.

    ix) Then lie on back with the knees drawn up and massage from the right side of the body to the left.

        (1) Turn over, lying on the left side, and massage the left side with a downward motion.

        (2) You should now be ready to eject the water.

x) The best time to do an enema is before retiring.

d) External Bath

    i) It is not necessary to take daily hot water baths with soap and a brush under normal conditions.

    ii) The morning "cold shower" during the entire year is not advisable.

        (1) There is no need to subject the body to an extreme shock.

        (2) In a number of cases, more harm than good may result.

    iii) Keep the skin clean so that the pores can function properly.

    iv) Ehret's water bathing instructions.

        (1) Place a basin of cool water in front of you.

        (2) Dip hands in the basin and then start briskly rubbing the face.

        (3) Wet the hands and apply to the neck and shoulders.

        (4) Rub the chest, stomach, arms, back, legs, and feet.

        (5) Put feet right into the basin if desired.

        (6) Keep moistening the hands as needed.

        (7) To dry off, rub with bare hands for 5 minutes until the body glows.

            (a) Or wipe off with a towel.

        (8) Do this upon rising, after exercising.

        (9) If you prefer a tub bath, then allow about one inch of cold water to run into the tub.

            (a) Sit in it with knees drawn up.

            (b) Follow the same rule of rubbing and massaging.

    v) Air bathing.

        (1) Remember that the air bath is just as important as the water bath.

        (2) A few minutes a day spent before an open window.

            (a) After arising and before bed when clothes are removed.

            (b) Massage the body to help the skin to retain its natural functioning qualities.

e) Ehret says, "Always bear in mind that extremes of any kind are harmful. This applies to exercise, bathing, and sleeping, as well as extremes in eating. Even extreme joy and happiness has been known to kill just as readily as extreme anger, hate, and worry. Therefore, AVOID EXTREMES OF ALL KINDS."

Glossary: Lesson XXV

Exercise: Activity demanding physical effort, often carried out to sustain or improve health and fitness.

Sunbathing: The act of sitting or lying in the sun.

Internal Bath (Enemas): A procedure in which liquid is injected into the rectum to expel uneliminated encumbrances. For more details about doing enemas, see the section on lemon juice enemas in *Spira Speaks: Dialogs and Essays on the Mucusless Diet Healing System*.

Bathing (Water): To wash or immerse the body in water for the purpose of cleansing.

Air Bath: A hygienic exposure of the body to the open air.

Review Questions: Lesson XXV

1. According to Ehret, what are the most natural forms of exercise?

2. Ehret claims that physical treatments can be combined with the Mucusless Diet to hasten the elimination. (True or False) If so, are there any cautions?

3. What are the benefits of sunbathing?

4. What are the benefits of enemas (internal baths)?

5. What kind of juice do some 21st-century practitioners add to their enemas?

6. Distilled water should be used for an enema. (True or False)

7. How do you take an "air bath"?

Further Reading: Lesson XXV

Spira, Prof. 2017. *Spira Speaks: Dialogs and Essays on the Mucusless Diet Healing System*. Columbus, OH: Breathair Publishing.

Ehret, Arnold. 2017. *Prof. Arnold Ehret's Physical Fitness Thru a Superior Diet, Fasting, and Dietetics*. Columbus, OH: Breathair Publishing.

A Message to Ehretists

Summary: A Message to Ehretists

In Ehret's concluding gesture, he highlights several fundamental points related to his *Mucusless Diet Healing System*. He affirms that disease is the result of uneliminated and decayed food substances, and that simply knowing the right foods to eat is not sufficient to cleanse and heal. Ehret shares his own personal testimony of an experience he had following a strict mucus-free diet for 2 years and one day consuming a large amount of grapes and grape juice. After a series of negative symptoms, he explains that he experienced a significant elimination and felt better than ever. Through his testimony, Ehret endeavored to demonstrate his theory of Vitality = Power − Obstruction, pointing out that he had a surge of energy as soon as the obstructions were eliminated. Ehret closes by saying that if the Garden of Eden existed, it must have been a fruit orchard. He explains that for thousands of years humans have been tricked into unconscious suicide and reduced to slavery in service to the destructive diet of civilization. He asserts that peace on earth remains a foolish dream as long as an unnatural mucus-forming diet remains standard for billions of people. Ehret concludes that it is of the utmost importance that the reader heed his message and spread it to a suffering and unhappy humankind.

Summary: A Message to Ehretists

1) In light of the previous lessons, Ehret implores that the reader should now be aware that disease consists of unknown, decayed, and fermented masses of matter in the body.

   a) The reader should know how ignorant it is to think that simply knowing the right foods to eat is enough.

   b) None of the recognized authorities know the importance of a thorough and deep cleansing of the human "cesspool."

      i) Most are fooled by Mother Nature.

2) Ehret's Testimony

   a) Ehret tells a story of being on a strict mucus-free diet for 2 years and one day eating two pounds of sweet grapes and drinking a gallon of fresh grape juice.

      i) At first he felt as if he would die.

         (1) Symptoms included: heart palpitations, extreme dizziness, severe pains in the stomach and intestines, etc.

      ii) After 10 minutes, a great event happened—a mucus-foaming diarrhea and vomiting of grape juice mixed with acid-smelling mucus.

      iii) Afterward, he felt so good that he performed the knee-bending and arm-stretching exercises 326 times consecutively.

      iv) All obstructions had been removed.

3) Final Thoughts

   a) Ehret says, "If the Garden of Eden—heaven on earth—ever existed it must have been a "fruit orchard." For thousands of years, through wrong civilization, humans have been tricked into unconscious suicide, reduced to slavery, to produce wrong food, 'earning their bread by the sweat of their brow.' Unnatural foods cause sickness and death."

   b) "Peace on Earth" happiness and righteousness as yet remain a foolish dream on the current diet.

   c) Ehret asserts that for the first time in history, he has shown that the diet of Paradise is not only possible, but is the "Unconditional Necessity" and first step to real salvation and redemption from the misery of life.

      i) "That it is a needed key to the lost paradise where disease, worry, and sorrow—hate, fight, and murder—were unknown, and where there was no death, from unnatural causes at least."

   d) Ehret concludes, "This book represents an outline of the serious nature of my work and it also appeals to you for help in carrying it through as the greatest deed you can perform—upon which depends not only your future destiny, but that of a suffering, unhappy humankind—on the verge of physical and mental collapse."

Glossary: A Message to Ehretists

Garden of Eden (or often Paradise): The biblical "Garden of God" described most notably in the Book of Genesis and the Book of Ezekiel, is where God intended Adam and Eve to dwell in peaceful and contented innocence, effortlessly reaping the fruits of the Earth. Within the story, fruit was plentiful, and God told Adam and Eve that they could eat and live off of almost all of the fruit in the garden, except the "forbidden fruit" from the "tree of knowledge of good and evil." When they disobeyed and ate the forbidden fruit, God drove them from paradise, ushering in the "Fall of Man." In the parlance, "Garden of Eden" is any state or place of complete peace and fulfillment.

Peace on Earth (or World Peace): The biblical context of the term refers to the Annunciation to the Shepherds in which angels tell a group of shepherds about the birth of the anointed one (the Christ). In present times, the phrase has come to represent the ideal state of freedom, peace, harmony, and happiness among all the peoples and nations of the world. There exist numerous theories and philosophies on the ways and means for Peace on Earth to come into existence. Ehret affirms that Peace on Earth remains a foolish dream until humans return to a natural diet of mucus-free foods, thereby rejecting any philosophy that purports to engender world peace without the mucus-free diet being at its foundation.

Salvation: Preservation or deliverance from harm, ruin, or loss.

"You Are What You Eat": Proverb that means one's health and wellness will be in accordance with what they choose to consume. Although the exact source is unknown, one of the first variations of the phrase in modern times comes from the French politician and writer Anthelme Brillat-Savarin's 1826 work *Physiologie du Goût, ou Méditations de Gastronomie Transcendante (The Physiology of Taste, or, Meditations on Transcendental Gastronomy)*, in which he writes, "Tell me what you eat and I will tell you what you are." German philosopher Ludwig Andreas Feuerbach used a variation of this metaphorical expression in his 1863–4 essay "Concerning Spiritualism and Materialism" where he writes, "Man is what he eats."

Purgatory: From Medieval Latin *purgatorium*, "means of cleansing," Ehret uses the term to apply a biblical undertone to the purging and purifying properties of fasting and mucus-free diet. In Judeo-Christian theology, fire or flame often represents purification, holiness, and divine love.

Review Questions: A Message to Ehretists

1. Explain what happened to Ehret after 2 years of a strict mucus-free diet.

2. (Short essay) Unpack and analyze the significance and implications of the following statement by Arnold Ehret: "I have proven for the first time in history that the diet of Paradise is not only possible—good enough for degenerate humankind, such as we now are—but that it is the Unconditional Necessity and the first step to real salvation and redemption from the misery of life. That it is a needed key to the lost paradise where disease, worry, and sorrow—hate, fight, and murder—were unknown, and where there was no death, from unnatural causes at least."

Review Questions (Spira's Answers)

Review Questions: Arnold Ehret's Biography

1. What is the name of the so-called incurable disease that Arnold Ehret suffered from?

   Bright's Disease (inflammation of the kidneys).

2. What prevented Ehret from traveling back to Europe when he visited the U.S. in 1914?

   World War I prevented Ehret from returning to Europe.

3. Arnold Ehret was a leader in what some historians call the "Back-to-Nature Renaissance." (True or False)

   True.

4. Today, an increased number of people are learning about Ehret's teachings and adopting plant-based, mucus-free lifestyles. (True or False)

   True.

Review Questions: Lesson I (Answers)

1. How does Arnold Ehret define disease?

   Ehret affirms that all forms of disease or sickness, no matter what names are given to them by medical scientists, are due to constipation. Thus, Ehret defines disease as constipation.

2. How does Ehret define constipation?

   Ehret defines constipation as a clogging up of the entire pipe system of the human body with waste derived from undigested, uneliminated, and unnatural food substances accumulated since childhood.

3. According to Ehret, how many pounds of uneliminated fecal matter is in the typical person?

   Ehret affirms that the average person has as much as 10 pounds of uneliminated feces in the bowels, continually poisoning their bloodstreams.

4. According to Ehret, humans can be healed by using special menus or radically long fasts. (True or False. Why or why not?)

False. Ehret asserts that it is wrong and ignorant to believe that an illness can be healed using special menus or radically long fasts. He explains that this is because each patient must apply the "systematic" methods of his *Healing System,* and that special considerations must be made for each individual case.

5. According to Ehret, what is "Nature's infallible law and omnipotent healing process"?

Ehret asserts that "fasting" is "Nature's only and infallible law." He adds that the "Mucusless Diet" is also governed by the principles of this law.

6. Ehret says, "whatever simple reason cannot grasp is humbug, however scientific it may sound." What do you think is meant by this statement?

Ehret's aforementioned statement of wisdom is intended to empower his readers to think for themselves and not fall prey to the complex nomenclatures and figures used by medical scientists and dietitians. Ehret implies that, although humans in the Western world are acclimatized to unconditionally respect the complicated language, and perceived authority, of medical and naturopathic practitioners, most of these practitioners are lost when it comes to helping people heal themselves of diet-related illness.

7. Why are Fasting and the Mucusless Diet often not successful in many cases?

Ehret explains that fasting and Mucusless Diet are often unsuccessful because 1) they are not used systematically in accordance with the condition of the patient, and 2) the inexperienced person that experiments with the Mucusless Diet or fasting does not know enough about the eliminative process, how long it requires, how to make gradual changes to one's diet, and what it means to cleanse the body of decades of waste. Without knowledge of the healing process, experimenters make wrong assumptions that lead to problematic decisions.

Review Questions: Lesson II (Answers)

1. Drugs always eventually eliminate from the body after taken. (True or False) Explain.

False. According to Ehret, the residue of drugs is not fully eliminated, but stored in the body for decades unless the patient safely eliminates it using Ehret's cleansing methods.

2. Describe what happens when dissolved chemical poisons from drugs are taken back into the circulation.

When the chemical poisons of drugs are dissolved and taken back into the circulation for elimination through the kidneys, unpleasant symptoms may be experienced. Common symptoms include extreme nervousness, dizziness, excessive heartbeats, and headaches.

3. What is the difference between latent and acute illness/disease?

Latent illness refers to illnesses that are hidden or dormant. Eventually these latent accumulations may emerge. Acute illness refers to any illness that develops quickly, is intense, and lasts a relatively short period of time. If the condition persists, the illness may then be considered chronic.

4. What happens when latent disease matter is stirred up in the body?

When latent disease matter is stirred up, for example by a cold, great amounts of mucus are expelled as the body makes an effort to free the most vital organs from waste.

5. What are the contents of disease/human illness, according to Ehret?

According to Ehret, mucus, pus, uric acid, toxins, drugs, uneliminated food substances, un-evacuated feces, etc. are the contents of human illness.

6. What do cold- and flu-like symptoms indicate?

According to Ehret, cold- and flu-like symptoms indicate Nature's cleansing process going deeper into the system in order to remove waste materials.

Review Questions: Lesson III (Answers)

1. What does Ehret mean by the word "diagnosis"?

Ehret uses the term "diagnosis" to refer to the art of analyzing the internal uncleanliness of the human body. The best ways to apply the components of the *Mucusless Diet Healing System* may be determined using these analytical methods.

2. Healing with the Mucusless Diet requires individual specialization for each patient. (True or False). Why or why not?

True. Ehret explains that the Mucusless Diet requires a significant amount of individual specialization to address the continually changing needs of the patient. This is because each person has unique physiological circumstances that demand different applications of Ehret's teachings.

3. What happens to human urine when a cleansing diet is applied, or fasting practiced?

As soon as one improves their diet or fasts a little, shocking waste materials can be found eliminated in the urine. This filtered waste should cause the urine to become cloudy.

4. What can be found in the colons of many people who have never cleansed?

Foreign matter, worms, and decades-old feces-stones may be found in the colons of people who have never cleansed. Further, the inside walls of the over-intestines may be encrusted by old, hardened feces.

5. Why does Ehret compare the human intestine to a filthy stovepipe?

A stovepipe is a pipe taking the smoke and gases from a stove up through a roof or to the chimney. Over time, grime and various uneliminated materials can accumulate in the pipe, causing obstructions. Ehret makes the connection between an encumbered stovepipe and constipated gastrointestinal tract.

6. What is the aim of Ehret's method of constitutional diagnosis?

The aim of Ehret's diagnostic method is to determine 1) the amount of waste in the body, 2) the type of waste in the body, 3) the amount of pus present and if drugs were used, 4) if internal organs are in the process of decomposition, and 5) how much the vitality of the patient has been compromised by their illnesses.

7. What is pus? What is albumen?

Pus refers to a thick white, yellowish, or greenish opaque liquid produced in infected tissue, consisting of dead blood cells and other debris. Within the Mucusless Diet, animal products are considered "pus-forming" because they degrade into pus within the body. Albumen is a class of simple, water-soluble proteins that can be coagulated by heat and are found in egg whites, blood serum, milk, and many other animal and plant tissues. Albuminous foods decompose into pus inside the body.

Review Questions: Lesson IV (Answers)

1. Name and describe the two body types identified by Ehret.

Arnold Ehret categorizes human physiology into two main types: fat and lean. People with lean physiologies are said to have "high metabolisms," and can seemingly eat a lot of food and not gain any weight. Ultimately, their body handles mucus and pus differently than someone with a fat type of physiology. The bodies of people with fatty physiologies can easily become mechanically obstructed. According to Ehret, these individuals do not have as much chemical interference as lean types. They are often overeaters of starchy foods.

2. Which physiological type is often a one-sided meat eater?

Lean type.

3. When examining a patient's "disease story," what are the primary questions you should ask?

According to Ehret, the primary questions to ask include 1) How long have you been sick? 2) What did the doctor call your disease? 3) What was the nature of the treatment? 4) How much and what kinds of treatment were taken? 5) Have you been operated on in the past? 6) What other kinds of treatment have you taken before?

4. What are the most important issues to consider regarding someone's "disease story"?

Ehret explains that the most important issues to consider include 1) the patient's current diet, 2) if they have special cravings for certain foods, 3) if they have bad living habits, and 4) if they are having regular natural bowel movements, and if not how long it has been since their last one. Ehret adds that it is important to base the change of diet on the patient's present diet and only a slight change toward an improved diet is recommended in the beginning.

5. According to Ehret, what is the most exact and unerring way to experimentally examine a patient's condition?

Ehret affirms that a short fast is the most effective way to discover the nature of one's illnesses and general internal uncleanliness.

6. Describe Ehret's thoughts about mental illness.

Ehret proposes that anyone suffering from mental illness has congestion of the brain, especially from gas pressure. He claims that insanity can be healed through fasting.

Review Questions: Lesson IVa (Answers)

1. What is the magic mirror? How is the magic mirror used with Ehret's "Experimental Diagnosis"?

The "Magic Mirror" is a term coined by Arnold Ehret to describe a diagnostic method of analyzing the surface of the tongue during or after a short fast to surmise the level of internal uncleanliness. A coated tongue is evidence of waste throughout the entire system. Ehret affirms that after a 2- to 3-day fast, the tongue, breath, and other symptoms will reveal the overall condition of the inside of the body.

2. It will take about 21 days of fasting and natural diet to totally cleanse the body of "foreign matter." (True or False) Explain.

False. Ehret says that it may take 1 to 3 years of systematic cleansing to cleanse old foreign matter from the body.

3. According to Ehret, what does meat decompose into in the body?

Pus.

4. Why is it dangerous to try and fast until the tongue is clean?

131

Given that it may require 1 to 3 years to clean the body of foreign matter, it is dangerous to try and fast until the tongue is clean. Ehret warns that it is important to put the magic mirror analysis into proper perspective and not become obsessed with it.

5. According to Ehret, what negative effects can result from taking drugs when sick?

Drugs can prevent the body from healing naturally and cause an illness to become chronic.

Review Questions: Lesson V (Answers)

1. What does Ehret call the "Formula of Life"?

V (Vitality) = P (Power) − O (Obstruction) or Vitality equals Power minus Obstruction.

2. Explain what is meant by V = P − O.

V = P − O is an equation created by Arnold Ehret that stands for Vitality equals Power minus Obstruction. Vitality stands for life, Power is that which perpetuates life, and Obstruction is that which inhibits or stops life. Materially, "Obstruction" represents bodily encumbrances from mucus-forming foods that slow or halt the utilization of oxygen in the body. Ehret asserts that mucus-forming foods create blockages in the body, and that a diet consisting of starchless/fat-free fruits and green-leaf vegetables is the only group of foods that do not leave behind obstructive residues. Furthermore, these foods will aid the body during the process of natural healing.

3. According to Ehret, what kind of fuel does the human body run on?

Ehret asserts that the human body is an "air-gas engine" that primarily runs on breathing air.

4. Why does vitality not rely on only eating "the right foods"?

Ehret proposes that vitality does not depend primarily on the right foods, especially if the best foods (fruits) are eaten in a body filled with toxic waste. When good foods are mixed with bad, he explains that the body cannot absorb the good qualities of the foods.

5. Extreme exercise and vibrating the body is important for eliminating internal waste (True or False). Why?

False. Ehret points out that you can artificially increase Power temporarily and remove some obstructions through extreme exercise, but that it is done at the expense of vitality while harming the rubber-like elasticity of the tissues. Thus, extreme exercise is not an optimal way to eliminate waste from the body.

6. Why do patients often fall back onto a "wrong" mucus-forming diet after eating mucusless or after a long fast?

Patients fall back onto the wrong diet because they attempt to move too rapidly through their transition, fast too radically, and therefore remove "O" (Obstructions) too quickly. They might feel good for a while, but horrible when they encounter an inevitable healing crisis. When weakness and fatigue set in, they lose hope and fall back onto a mucus-rich diet.

7. According to Ehret, the lungs act as a pump and heart as a valve. (True or False)

True.

8. What happens to the human body when it has more "obstruction" than "power"?

The body comes to a standstill. In other words, death occurs.

Review Questions: Lesson VI (Answers)

1. According to Ehret, why does the circulation increase while running or climbing a mountain?

According to Ehret, these activities cause a person to increase their breathing (air pressure), which then speeds circulation and therefore the heart rate.

2. Why does Ehret find standard theories of metabolism to be "absurd"?

Ehret finds standard metabolism theories absurd because they are the foundation of the wrong cell theory and albumen theory, which posits the idea that the cells of the body are continually used up and need to constantly be replaced with high-protein foods. Ehret has found this to not only be wrong, but promulgate eating habits that result inevitably in illness.

3. Why is it easier for internally clean people to fast?

If Ehret is correct, and the operation of the body depends on having a vessel with the least amount of obstructions to utilize oxygen fully, it would then follow that lean people with fewer physical obstructions could fast easier. This is a logical conclusion of Ehret's Vitality = Power − Obstruction (V = P − O) formula.

4. How many days was Ehret's longest record-breaking fast?

49 days.

5. What does Ehret's long fast prove or suggest?

It proves that humans are air-gas engines and suggests that the body does not require the constant replacement of certain nutritional constituents to survive or thrive, such as protein- or fat-containing foods.

Review Questions: Lesson VII (Answers)

1. High-protein foods act as _____ for a certain period of time. (Fill in the blank).

Stimulation.

2. According to Ehret, when people become sick it is important that they eat high-protein foods to maintain their strength. (True or False) Why or why not?

False. Ehret points out that the strength of a sick person can actually increase during a period of fasting or when removing protein-rich foods from one's diet. Recommending protein-rich foods to a sick person is to suggest a course of action diametrically opposed to Nature's laws of healing.

3. According to Ehret, what type of food are humans biologically designed to eat?

Fruit.

4. It is a widely known fact that cows drink milk and eat the flesh of other cows to help them produce their own milk and flesh (beef). (True or False) Why or why not?

False. Adult cows are herbivores and do not drink other cows' milk or eat beef to produce their own flesh.

5. According to Ehret, why can a one-sided meat eater sometimes live longer than a vegetarian over-eater?

The reason a "one-sided" meat eater can live a relatively longer time than the starch-eating vegetarian is because the latter produces more physical obstructions in the body, preventing oxygen utilization and blood flow. The meager meat eater produces less physical obstructions, but increases chemical interference in the body, which can lead to tragic long-term consequences.

Review Questions: Lesson VIII (Answers)

1. The oxidation of iron in the blood causes it to turn it become what color?

> Oxidation turns the blood red inside of the body, and a dark red or rusty brown outside the body.

2. Dr. Thomas Powell and Arnold Ehret both believe that white blood corpuscles defend the body from diseases. (True or False) Explain.

3. According to Ehret, how do mucus and toxemias affect the color of the skin?

> Ehret believed that the "mineral salts" responsible for skin pigmentation are lacking in lighter-skinned people, and that their pores are constipated with white, dry mucus. According to Ehret, once the blood is cleansed from waste materials, the practitioner's hue can substantially darken.

4. What happens to mucus-forming foods when they sit for long periods of time in the intestines?

> As demonstrated by Ehret's Acidic & Mucus-Forming Diet Test, mucus-forming foods become fetid, slimy, and fermenting like an unclean garbage can.

5. What is the name of a book written by Julius Hensel referenced by Arnold Ehret in the *Mucusless Diet Healing System*?

> Julius Hensel's *Life: Its Foundation and the Means for Its Preservation*.

Review Questions: Lesson IX (Answers)

1. According to Ehret, what kinds of foods create vital human blood?

> Fruit.

2. Most carnivorous animals in Nature cook their food in order to be able to digest it. (True or False) Explain.

> False. No flesh-eating animal in Nature cooks its meals.

3. Clean blood is able to dissolve and eliminate waste better than obstructed blood. (True or False) Explain.

> True. According to Ehret, the goal of the *Healing System* is to help build cleaner blood better able to dissolve and eliminate waste in the body.

4. According to Ehret, why are processed foods of all kinds unhealthy?

Because manufactured and processed foods do not build human blood, and only serve to "stimulate" the eater at the expense of leaving behind obstructive and poisonous waste materials.

Review Questions: Lesson X (Answers)

1. What are the two main categories that Ehret divides all healing practices into?

Ehret divides healing practices into two categories: medicine and drugless healing.

2. According to Ehret, why do symptoms of illness often return after medical treatments?

Many medical treatments include the use of pharmaceutical medications, which Ehret identifies as being poisonous. When a new and dangerous poison is introduced into the circulation of a sick person, the elimination is more or less stopped because the body instinctively sets to work on neutralizing the new poisons. The symptoms, however, come back again at a later date because the excess waste was not eliminated or an improved diet adopted and sustained.

3. List three physical treatments.

Three physical treatments include exercise, stretching, and breathing exercises. (Other answers include massage, osteopathy, physical therapy, electricity, electric light therapy, sunlight, etc.)

4. What is Ehret's opinion of exclusively using mental treatments?

Ehret finds mental treatments better than medical or psychiatric, insofar as they do not prescribe drugs. However, he explains that such attempts at treatment can keep people in ignorance of what disease truly is and how it can be healed. For instance, it would not make sense to pray for good health, while continuing to break Nature's dietary laws through the continued eating of pus- and mucus-forming foods.

Review Questions: Lesson XI (Answers)

1. Nuts are mucus-forming. (True or False) Explain.

True. In Lesson XI, the author says, "All fruits, raw or cooked; also nuts and green-leaf vegetables are mucus-free." However, this statement contradicts what is said elsewhere in the *Mucusless Diet* book. One instance is in Lesson XVI on the Transition Diet, where Ehret writes, "Other kinds of grated nuts or nut butter may be served once in a while for this purpose (transition diet), but are too rich in protein and will produce, if continually used, mucus and uric acid." Based on Ehret's recommendations, use nuts sparingly; it may be understood that they are mucus-forming.

(Extended answer: In Lesson XXII, Ehret says that "All nuts are too rich in protein and fat and should be eaten only in winter, and then too, only sparingly." Ehret clearly explains in Lesson XXII, "All fats are acid-forming, even those of vegetable origin, and are not used by the body." Despite the contradiction, Prof. Spira affirms that nuts are mucus-forming based on Ehret's statements that they are too high in protein and fat. However, they can be used for transitional purposes, as indicated by Ehret.)

2. According to Ehret, the average person and doctor often blame disease on many things other than diet. (True or False).

True.

3. Ehret divides all foods into what two categories?

The two categories are 1) natural and healing foods (mucus-free foods), versus 2) harmful and disease-producing foods (pus- and mucus-forming foods).

4. What is "systematic" about the *Mucusless Diet Healing System*?

The major elements of the "system" include 1) the proper rate of change toward mucus-free foods based on the individual practitioner's physiological circumstances; 2) properly combining foods to aid elimination; and 3) how long and how often fasting is utilized. In later lessons, Ehret stresses the importance of incorporating ancillary therapies into the "system," including internal baths (enemas), exercise, and other natural hygiene methods.

5. What did Arnold Ehret mean by his concept that "Life is a tragedy of Nutrition"?

Historically, the word tragedy referred to a play or other serious literary work with an unhappy ending. Later, it was also used to identify unhappy events or disasters. As evidenced by Ehret's rejection of nutritional concepts, it seems that the "tragedy of nutrition" is not about the lack, or poor choice of, nutritious foods. One way to view it is that the "tragedy" is that the concept of nutrition 1) erroneously exists and 2) is dietetically opposed to the truth of natural laws governing animal life on earth. In other words, the tragedy is not only that people eat poorly and die, but think that they are eating healthy, or taking drugs responsibly, and die not realizing that pus- and mucus-forming foods and drugs are the foundation of their demise. Ehret insists that the confusion and ignorance of diet are so great that they are the "missing link" of the human mind.

Review Questions: Lesson XII (Answers)

1. Explain why Ehret said that vegetarianism could be worse than a meat-based diet.

Ehret explains that a vegetarian diet only omits meat, and the users of the eating method use improper mixtures of foods—including large amounts of fruit with eggs, milk, etc. Such mixtures could cause overeating, which leads to increased obstruction in the body. As pointed out in Lesson V, when "Obstruction" becomes more than the "Power" needed to function, the human body comes to a standstill.

2. Explain Ehret's views on the "raw-food diet."

Ehret affirms that the "raw-food diet" represents progress, but provides the wrong reasoning for why raw foods are good. He claims that this poor reasoning leads to "fanatic extremes." According to Ehret, raw foodists claim that all cooking destroys food (nutritional) values, yet Ehret explains, "wrong cooking destroys healing value qualities" of food. In other words, Ehret does not believe that raw foods are beneficial because they are nutritious, but because the rough fiber can relieve constipation.

3. What is a "camouflaged fast"? Give at least one example.

Any method of eating or drinking that allows the stomach and intestines to have a rest—similar to the break that the system receives during a fast. Such methods are often not viewed as a "fast," and if continued can be harmful, depending on the method. Ehret cites Fletcherism (long-term chewing of every bite), the Salisbury cure (eating one small piece of beefsteak and toast per day), the milk diet (fasting on milk), and the Schroth cure (eating dry bread for several days followed by a day of liquid and some food) as camouflaged fasts.

4. According to Ehret, radical fruit fasts without a systematic transition are irrational and potentially dangerous. (True or False).

True.

5. Why is milk dieting dangerous?

Ehret affirms that milk-dieting enthusiasts ultimately suffer from terrible constipation because milk is an extremely mucus-forming item.

Review Questions: Lesson XIII (Answers)

1. Why do raw mucus-free foods act "mysteriously" to the average person, who ultimately blames fruit or mucus-free vegetables for their ailments?

The average person, who does not understand the healing process, blames mucus-free foods for their newfound ailments instead of recognizing that the ingested mucus-free foods are mixing with existing waste materials. The average person does not understand that their symptoms may first become worse while waste materials are being stirred up and eliminated.

2. It is important to stick to special menus while practicing the Mucusless Diet. (True or False) Explain.

> False. Ehret affirms that the *Mucusless Diet Healing System* is not just a series of menus or list of what foods should be eaten, but a "system" in which every change of diet has significance and must be made in accordance with the patient. Certain menus may be used as tools of the system, but changes must be made based on the shifting physiological condition of the patient.

3. Why is the *Mucusless Diet Healing System* not like a medical prescription?

> Ehret explains that the *Mucusless Diet Healing System* is not like a prescription of drugs, but rather a system of dietetic changes and improvements that lead to the elimination of poisonous materials and the revitalization of the blood in the patient's body.

Review Questions: Lesson XIV (Answers)

1. Why did Ehret include Ragnar Berg's table in his original *Mucusless Diet*, although he knew it was flawed?

> According to Prof. Spira, Ehret includes it to show that he was not alone in believing that acid-forming foods, many of which are inherently mucus-forming, are harmful to the body.

2. According to Prof. Spira, what is the problem with the Ragnar Berg table?

> According to Prof. Spira, the problem is that many of the items on the original table are actually very much acid- and mucus-forming, although listed as "acid-binding." This has confused many readers who assumed that all foods listed as "acid-binding" were mucus-free and okay to eat.

3. Are all the mucus-free items on Spira's list recommended as good to eat? (True or False) Explain.

> False. Prof. Spira affirms that it is not a list of what foods he recommends to eat, but an objective look at what foods are and are not mucus-forming or acid-forming. He explains that just because a food item is technically "mucus-free" does not mean it is good to eat.

4. What is meant by "slightly mucus-forming"?

> "Slightly mucus-forming" refers to foods that may leave behind a small amount of mucus residue if not promptly eliminated from the body. Some of these foods may be recommended during periods of the transition diet.

5. What does "potentially acid-forming" mean? Give one example.

> "Potentially acid-forming" refers to foods that do not leave behind mucus residue, but may or may not cause harm when ingested due to their acid-forming properties. Examples from the

Annotated Mucusless Diet include black peppercorns, cayenne pepper, chili powder, cream of tartar, curry powder, nutmeg, paprika, pepper, salt (celery, crystal, iodized, sea), vanilla extract, and pasteurized fruit juices.

6. What are "acid-forming stimulants"?

"Acid-forming stimulants" are food items that may not be explicitly mucus-forming, but can cause harm when ingested due to their acid-forming properties.

Review Questions: Lesson XV (Answers)

1. Why is it not good to drink or eat chunky soups?

Soups that include solid vegetables combined with warm or cool liquid are hard to digest and complicate the elimination process. Soups, whether they have solid elements or not, should be avoided with meals containing solid food.

2. Why should drinking be avoided during meals? What should be done instead?

Combining liquid with solid foods makes it hard for the body to properly digest and eliminate waste. If someone feels the need to drink with, or near, a meal they should do so well before or after it is eaten.

3. Fats of all kinds should be avoided. (True or False) Explain.

True. Ehret affirms that fats are unnatural and therefore should not be eaten. If fats are craved, he recommends using a nut butter on well-toasted 100% grain bread which should be eaten toward the end of the vegetable meal.

4. Why is it important for a diet of healing to be digested and eliminated from the body quickly?

This is because a diet of healing has the potential to loosen and dissolve waste, debris, mucus, and other poisons, which are thrown back into the circulation. To avoid unnecessary unpleasantness, it is important that the contents of each meal be eliminated efficiently and within as short a period of time as is reasonably possible.

5. What does Ehret mean by saying that the vegetable meal should create a "broom"?

One fundamental goal of Ehret's vegetable-based meals is to supply what he calls the "broom" to mechanically cleanse the digestive tract of waste. This is done using raw, baked, and stewed starchless vegetables. Ehret emphasizes that this broom is important for eliminating stored-up poisons loosened during the body's housecleaning.

6. What does the term "mucus-lean" mean?

The term "mucus-lean" refers to the period of one's transition when some mucus-forming foods are partially used.

7. Describe the main components of "Ehret's Standard Combination Salad."

Ehret's Standard Combination salad may include raw grated carrots or coleslaw, or an equal portion of each, and two or three spoonsful of a stewed or canned vegetable, such as green peas, string beans, or spinach. Add to this one of the following items (whatever is in season): cucumbers, tomatoes, green onions, lettuce, or other green-leaf vegetables, celery, etc. A vinegar-free dressing may be added for flavoring. The rest of the meal should be baked or stewed vegetables, such as cauliflower, beets, parsnips, turnips, squash, etc.

Review Questions: Lesson XVI (Answers)

1. According to Ehret, what is the most natural food for humans? Why is it not advisable to eat this way in the beginning?

Ehret asserts that the ideal and most natural method of eating for humans is one kind of fresh fruit that is in season. Although he identifies this as natural, he emphasizes the importance of using his "transition diet" methodology to evolve toward the ideal diet. Furthermore, given that one type of fruit in season is best, Ehret encourages the reader to eat as simply as possible, regardless of what phase of the transition a person is practicing.

2. Why are cooked foods used during the transition diet?

Ehret recommends cooked foods during the transition diet to make certain vegetables and fruits more digestible, and in some cases palatable.

3. How should someone eat in the beginning of their transition if they have great amount of acidity in their stomach?

For bad or very acidic stomachs, Ehret recommends employing menus consisting of more vegetables and less fruits. One combination he recommends for bad stomachs is as follows: "Take as stock 2/3 grated or shredded raw carrots, or grated celery or grated beets may be used, although carrots are best. Add 1/3 of finely sliced very ripe bananas and a few raisins or sliced dried figs."

4. Why are Ehret's methods different from most "raw foodist" approaches?

Ehret claims that he differs from "raw food 'fanatics'" because he is not concerned with the nutritional value of food when eating to heal. He affirms that it is more important that the patient enjoy their change of diet during the transition, until their tastes and conditions have improved.

5. Vinegar is an important part of the *Mucusless Diet*. (True or False) Explain.

141

False. Ehret recommends that lemon juice be used in place of vinegar.

6. Describe Ehret's "standard menu" in his sanitarium.

Ehret's "standard menu" consists of a drink in the morning, one or two kinds of fruit for lunch, and a mucus-free or mucus-lean, vegetable-based meal for dinner.

7. How can starchy foods be made less harmful through cooking?

Ehret explains that cooking can make starchy foods less harmful because the cooking process destroys or neutralizes, more or less, the sticky properties of the pasty starch.

Review Questions: Lesson XVII (Answers)

1. Why should fruits be eaten first (if fruits are mixed with other foods)?

Ehret explains that digestion of ripe fruits takes place in a normal stomach within a few minutes after eating. He recommends waiting 5 or 10 minutes before ingesting the vegetable course if eating fruit and vegetables in the same meal.

2. Why is it important to avoid drinking while eating?

Ehret affirms that liquids of all kinds (including soups) interfere with proper digestion of the meal. He advocates at least thirty minutes before drinking before or after a meal.

3. Why is it best not to eat countless mixtures?

Ehret affirms that simplicity is a fundamental principle and that humans should avoid complicated mixtures. More complicated mixtures are harder for humans to properly digest and eliminate.

4. A portion of the material from this lesson in the originally published Mucusless Diet was not written by Arnold Ehret. What portions were added, and what is the name of the person who presumably added them?

As indicated by the editor's note, presumably Fred Hirsch added a section reiterating some of Ehret's eating principles, sample menus, salad recipes, and cooked vegetable recipes. Since the 1924 edition, items in this section have been updated, first by Hirsch, and then by Prof. Spira in the annotated, edited, and revised edition of the *Mucusless Diet*.

5. Based on the salad recipes in the *Mucusless Diet* book, create your own combination salad. Refer back to the salad recipes in the Lesson XVII text if necessary, or come up with your own and compare it to Ehret's.

Similar to the "Natural Combination Salad," mix a large bowl of finely cut red-leaf lettuce, two handfuls of spinach, two chopped celery stalks, sliced cucumber, one diced tomato, and one handful of finely cut parsley. Add oil and lemon juice. Mix thoroughly.

Review Questions: Lesson XVIII (Answers)

1. Why do humans and many animals lose their appetites when sick?

   According to Ehret, it is an instinctual reaction to illness whereby the body is signaling the organism to fast or reduce the quantity of food and allow the body to heal.

2. Why do people blame weakness on the lack of food?

   Ehret explains that when one fasts, they initially eliminate the primary obstructions of wrong and excessive eating and feel good temporarily. Nevertheless, as the fast goes deeper, secondary obstructions from increased waste in the circulation cause the faster to feel miserable and in many cases weak. People blame the lack of food instead of the waste in their system.

3. Why does a faster's urine often turn cloudy?

   During a fast, it is common for mucus and other waste to be filtered by the kidneys, which should produce cloudy urine.

4. According to Ehret, fasting is a mechanical process whereby the tissue system contracts and presses out waste. (True or False)

   True.

5. Why is fasting initially a "negative proposition"?

   Ehret says that fasting is at first a negative proposition to relieve the body from direct obstructions of uneliminated food substances. In an encumbered body, these initial fasts can cause uncomfortable symptoms as the circulation contracts and waste starts to eliminate.

Review Questions: Lesson XIX (Answers)

1. How long should a person fast?

Ehret explains that the length of a person's fast cannot be predetermined, even in cases where the condition of the patient is known. When and how to break the fast is determined by considering the ways in which conditions change during the fasting period. Ehret affirms that the fast should be broken as soon as too much obstruction is entering into the circulation, and the blood needs new "vital substances" to resist and neutralize the poisons. In the *Mucusless Diet*, Ehret recommends starting with a 2- or 3-day fasting period.

2. Does Ehret recommend long-term fasting? Why or why not?

No, Ehret admonishes that the reader move away from the perception that "the longer you fast, the better the cure." He points out that humans are the "sickest animals on earth" and that shorter fasting periods interspersed with days of clean eating is preferable.

3. What symptoms may be experienced during a fast if drugs were ever taken by, or administered to, the patient?

Palpitation of the heart, headaches, nervousness, and insomnia are several symptoms common for fasters who have used, or had any kind of drug administered to them, in the past.

4. Describe Ehret's guidelines for fasting.

1) Prepare for an easier fast through a gradually changing diet toward a mucusless diet, as well as with natural laxatives and enemas. 2) Perform shorter fasts interspersed with days of eating a mucus-poor or mucus-free diet. 3) Be careful if drugs were used or administered, in which case a long, slowly changing, preparative diet is recommended.

5. Recall the two fasting case studies that Ehret shared in Lesson XIX. Describe one of them, and explain what Ehret said they should have done to avoid the fatal mistakes made.

Case Study #1—A one-sided meat eater suffering from diabetes broke a week-long fast with dates and died. Ehret explains that the horrible poisons loosened in the stomach during the fast were mixed with the concentrated fruit sugar of the dates, which created a shock to the system. According to Ehret, the correct approach would have been as follows: 1) A laxative should have been administered, then later raw and cooked starchless vegetables, a piece of rough bran bread/toast, and (optionally) sauerkraut; 2) no fruit should have been eaten for a long time after this person broke their fast; and 3) this patient should have better prepared through a much longer transition diet period.

Case Study #2—A man over 60 years of age fasted 28 days, and his first meal was vegetarian foods including boiled potatoes. An operation revealed that the potatoes were glued in place inside his intestines. Ehret explains that 1) this patient fasted much too long for a person of his age and without proper preparation; 2) hot compresses on the abdomen and high enemas might have helped the elimination, along with strong starchless, mostly raw, vegetables; and 3) no fruits should have been used for a considerable amount of time.

Review Questions: Lesson XX (Answers)

1. A fast should be broken with a meal that is sufficiently laxative. (True or False) Explain.

    True. Ehret affirms that the sooner the first meal passes through the body, the more efficiently it carries out the loosened mucus and poisons from the intestines and stomach. Thus, a meal with laxative qualities is required.

2. If a bowel movement is not had after a fast is broken, what should be done?

    If no good natural bowel movement is had after two or three hours, Ehret recommends helping with a natural laxative and/or enema.

3. What is meant by "Nature's operating table"?

    Ehret uses the expression "lying on Nature's operating table" to refer to the natural and noninvasive healing that occurs during the fasting process.

4. How much juice or lemonade may be consumed during a fasting day?

    Ehret says that the patient may drink up to two or three quarts of their fasting drinks for the entire day.

5. Why is a heavy breakfast so bad?

    Ehret observes that humans are essentially fasting while sleeping, thereby initiating the process of elimination. Thus, breaking one's nightly fast with a heavy meal aggressively stops this elimination with foods that do not eliminate well and cause unnecessary obstruction.

6. List two of Ehret's six rules to remember during periods of fasting.

    Include two from the following:

    1) Thoroughly clean the lower intestines with enemas, preferably every day.

    2) Before a longer fast, take a natural laxative occasionally, especially before the beginning of the fast.

    3) If possible, remain in the fresh air all day and night.

    4) Take a walk, exercise, or do some physical work only on days when strong enough to do so. Otherwise, sleep as much as possible.

5) On days when the patient feels weak and their sleep is restless, they should reread the fasting lessons and Lesson V over and over again.

6) Whenever the patient arises after lying down, it should be done slowly to avoid becoming dizzy.

Review Questions: Lesson XXI (Answers)

1. What is a "24-hour fast"?

Also called the "one-meal-a-day plan," it refers to only eating once a day. Ehret recommends eating in the afternoon around 3 or 4pm.

2. How should the length of one's fast be increased?

Ehret explains that the patient should start with the non-breakfast plan. Then follow with the 24-hour fast for a period of time. The fast can be gradually increased up to 3, 4, or 5 days, eating a mucus-free diet in-between for 1, 2, 3, or 4 days. Ehret explains that through this kind of intermittent fasting process, the blood is gradually improved, regenerated, and can more easily stand the poisons and waste being loosened, and is able at the same time to better dissolve and eliminate "disease deposits" from the deepest tissues of the body.

3. What is meant by the "Superior Fast"?

What Ehret means by the "Superior Fast" is somewhat elusive. Ehret said, "And if you simply supply the 'engine' with the necessary water that is used up, you ascend into a higher state of physical, mental, and spiritual condition. I call this the 'Superior Fast'." Some readers interpret this to mean that water fasting is a "Superior Fast." In other words, that Ehret infers that water needs to be replenished through drinking. Yet in Lesson V, Ehret asserted that the body is an "air-gas engine" that runs primarily on the breathing of air. Based on Ehret's arguments in this lesson, the "superior fast" may be viewed as a "dry fast," that is, no substances other than air taken into the body. However, "dry fasting" is not advocated by Ehret in the *Mucusless Diet* text. The idea of the "Superior Fast" is offered as a philosophical ideal to strive for and not a specific practice recommended to the reader.

4. What does Ehret claim will happen to your thoughts and aspirations after the cleansing of your body?

Ehret asserts that one's mind, ideals, aspirations, way of thinking, etc., will transform as a result of properly performed fasting.

Review Questions: Lesson XXII (Answers)

1. What is Ehret's opinion of scientific dietetics, food values, and their statistics?

   Ehret regards them as "trash" that is useless unless a food item is first evaluated by 1) how much disease matter (mucus) will it produce in the body and 2) the dissolving, eliminating, healing properties of the items.

2. Are avocados mucus-forming? Why or why not?

   Based on Ehret's statements about the harmful nature of fats, the excessive fat content in avocados makes them acid- or mucus-forming.

3. Does Arnold Ehret recommend using hard-boiled eggs?

   Although Ehret says that hard-boiled eggs are less harmful than regular eggs, because some of the gluey properties are destroyed, he does not ever explicitly recommend using hard-boiled eggs. In earlier editions of the Mucusless Diet, the editor Fred Hirsch includes one meal option in the Vegetarian recipe section with a hard-boiled egg. It should be made clear that Hirsch included the hard-boiled egg in a recipe and not Arnold Ehret.

4. Well-baked or well-fried sweet potatoes are close to being mucusless. (True or False)

   True.

5. According to Ehret, rice is one of the greatest mucus-forming foods. (True or False)

   True.

6. Can cereals be used during the transition? If so, how should they be prepared?

   Some cereal products are permissible for transitional purposes. Bran, graham, whole wheat, or rye bread are less harmful, especially when toasted or well baked.

7. Explain why nuts are mucus-forming. If eaten at all, how should they be eaten?

   Nuts are too rich in protein and fat, therefore acid- and mucus-forming. If eaten, nuts should always be combined with dried sweet fruits to aid with digestion.

8. Why do most pus- or mucus-forming foods need to be prepared or processed in order to eat?

   Most mucus-forming foods are unnatural for humans to eat and the process of preparing food makes them palatable and more digestible. For instance, Ehret affirms that humans could not eat fats or animal-based foods without the cook's "preparation," which he identifies as "the art to cover the real taste and odor by spices and dressings."

Review Questions: Lesson XXIII (Answers)

1. Ehret claims that sexual diseases can easily be healed through diet and fasting. (True or False)

    True.

2. Why does Ehret characterize some sex diseases as "colds" of the reproductive organs?

    This is because Ehret views diseases of the sexual organs as "eliminations," not unlike any other elimination that the body goes through due to illness.

3. What does Ehret mean when he says that humans of civilization are products of "stimulants" and not true love vibrations?

    Ehret infers that pus- and mucus-forming foods, which he identifies as stimulating poisons, cause humans to reproduce under the influence of poisonous, disease-producing foods. He asserts that in a clean body free of obstruction, genuine love vibrations could be fully emitted, felt, and appreciated.

4. What is Ehret's opinion of facial hair on men?

    Ehret regards the beard as a "secondary sex organ" and a sign of male strength and virility.

5. Why does Ehret claim that the Mucusless Diet and fasting are the only way to heal impotence?

    Ehret affirms that the Mucusless Diet is the only way to heal impotence because it is the only viable and safe way to remove the obstructive blockages to the circulation caused by improper diet that are the fundamental cause of the condition.

Review Questions: Lesson XXIV (Answers)

1. How did Ehret use the term "eugenics" differently than his peers? How might this confuse modern readers?

    Ehret used the term "eugenics" to make a philosophical point about the potential for developing an improved race of humans through the *Mucusless Diet Healing System*. For many modern readers, this term is off-putting due to its historical association with racist and genocidal policies in the United States, Canada, and various European countries in the early 20th century. Ehret wrote this text well before the climax of the most radical eugenic policies in the United States and by Hitler in Germany. Ehret's beliefs about a so-called superior race of people are diametrically opposed to the white supremacist mentality that was the foundation of most eugenic programs, insofar as he identifies darker skin as a sign of health.

2. What did Ehret recommend future parents to do?

Ehret explains that it is not advisable to start a radical change in diet during pregnancy or while nursing. He asserts that the principles of the *Mucusless Diet Healing System* should be started at least 2 or 3 months before conception.

3. What should a baby consume?

Ehret recommends that babies consume the mother's breast milk for as long as possible, provided that the mother has been cleansed for some time with the Mucusless Diet. He then recommends that the mother start feeding the baby with a teaspoonful of good fresh fruit juices diluted with water as soon as possible. Juice from stewed beets is also recommended.

4. What is meant by the statement that "humans were once a higher, superior kind of being, not a species of the monkey family"?

Philosophically, Ehret rejects the notion of Darwinian evolution (that humans evolved from the ape family) and suggests that the origin of humans comes from a higher plane. Ehret proposes that we "are only a shade of the original human, caused through our degeneration." This statement suggests that Ehret believes humans degenerated from a much more advanced human source.

Review Questions: Lesson XXV (Answers)

1. According to Ehret, what are the most natural forms of exercise?

Walking, hiking, dancing, and singing (natural breath exercise).

2. Ehret claims that physical treatments can be combined with the *Mucusless Diet* to hasten the elimination. (True or False) If so, are there any cautions?

True. However, the practitioner must take care to avoid overworking themselves on days of strong elimination.

3. What are the benefits of sunbathing?

The sunbath is an excellent "invisible" waste eliminator and rejuvenates the skin, causing it to naturally darken.

4. What are the benefits of enemas (internal baths)?

Ehret asserts that enemas help the sticky waste and slimy mucus, etc., which Nature is attempting to eject, to be removed from the body. As these poisons are eliminated, the patient will crave wrong foods less and less.

5. What kind of juice do some 21st-century practitioners add to their enemas?

Lemon juice.

6. Distilled water should be used for an enema. (True or False)

True.

7. How do you take an "air bath"?

An air bath can be performed for a few minutes a day in front of an open window or outside. It can be done after arising and before bed with clothing removed. The bather should massage the body, which will help the skin to retain its natural functioning qualities.

Review Questions: A Message to Ehretists (Answers)

1. Explain what happened to Ehret after 2 years of a strict mucus-free diet.

One day he ate two pounds of sweet grapes and drank a gallon of fresh grape juice, and then experienced an intense healing crisis. He had heart palpitations, extreme dizziness, and severe pains in the stomach and intestines, and he thought that he was going to die. After 10 minutes, a great event happened in which he eliminated a mucus-foaming diarrhea and vomited grape juice mixed with acid-smelling mucus. Afterward, he felt so good that he performed the knee-bending and arm-stretching exercises 326 times consecutively. This experience caused him to remove a great amount of obstructions, therefore affording him greater vitality.

2. (Short essay) Unpack and analyze the significance and implications of the following statement by Arnold Ehret: "I have proven for the first time in history that the diet of Paradise is not only possible—good enough for degenerate humankind, such as we now are—but that it is the Unconditional Necessity and the first step to real salvation and redemption from the misery of life. That it is a needed key to the lost paradise where disease, worry, and sorrow—hate, fight, and murder—were unknown, and where there was no death, from unnatural causes at least."

Ehret affirms that the Mucusless Diet (mucus-free fruits and green-leaf vegetables if desired) is the natural diet for humans. He proposes that our species can and will experience paradise again if this natural human diet is adopted. Ehret's statement implies that humans once lived a paradisiacal life free from pain, illness, and emotional suffering. Ehret was particularly inspired by the Judeo-Christian story of the Garden of Eden, although narratives of a golden age of paradise on earth are common within many mythological traditions (See Heinburg). Ehret's statement infers that the unnatural diet of civilization is not only the primary cause of humanity's diseased conditions, but the cause of humankind's misery and malevolence in general. He implies that hatred, fighting, murder, rape, racism, sexism, greed, all forms of violence, and injustice are the direct result of eating pus- and mucus-forming foods. In other words, the direct result of breaking the fundamental laws of Nature.

Ehret's statement that "there was no death, from unnatural causes at least," infers that Ehret believed that death is, perhaps, not natural. Or, at least that what is considered natural causes of death today are in fact unnatural. As long-term Mucusless Diet practitioner Willie Smart (aka Brother Air) put it, "how many people do you personally know who diet eating nothing but fruits and green-leaf vegetables throughout their life"?

In sum, Ehret's statement is one of hope for humanity. Through his Healing System and philosophy of healing, Ehret attempts to share information that he feels is the answer to the problems of humanity. He believes that the source of all problems in the world is an improper diet by humans. That the dysfunction of governments, police brutality, war, the mistreatment of the environment, the disregard for the lives of animals, etc., are all symptoms of an improper diet laden with mucus- and pus-forming foods.

How badly do we want to experience paradise? Are we content to live in ignorance and blame everything but diet? Is it easier to continue to believe the propaganda we've been fed? That we need to stuff ourselves with protein and fat? That we must eat certain nutritious foods, although we know they cause illness? Ehret challenges us to shift our paradigm away from the mucus-based status quo and extremism of the 21st century and embrace our true nature as mucus-free beings. Mucus-free is the key.

About Prof. Spira

In 2002, Prof. Spira was a 280-pound former high school football player suffering from multiple ailments such as daily migraine headaches, allergies, regular bouts of bronchitis, sleep apnea, persistent heartburn, etc. After having lost his mother to a terrible string of chronic illnesses when he was in the 6th grade, he grew up assuming that he was genetically destined to be sick his whole life. While studying jazz trombone performance at the University of Cincinnati's College Conservatory of Music, he met a jazz drummer named Willie Smart (aka Brother Air) who told him about Arnold Ehret's *Mucusless Diet Healing System*. Within 6 months of reading the book, Spira lost 110 pounds and overcame all of his major ailments. He was able to throw away his CPAP unit (an oxygen mask that treats sleep apnea) and the medications he had taken since childhood. Since his transformation, Spira has helped and inspired numerous people to use the mucusless diet to overcome their illnesses through his writings, music, and one-on-one consultations.

Spira is a professional jazz trombonist, educator, and author. He holds an MM in jazz trombone performance, an MA in African American and African Studies, and a PhD in musicology with a specialization in ethnomusicology from the Ohio State University. He is also the co-leader of an all-vegetarian and Ehretist jazz group entitled the Breathairean Ensemble, whose members are dedicated to inspiring their listeners to pursue what they call "physiological liberation." In 2013, Spira published his first book about the mucusless diet entitled *Spira Speaks: Dialogs and Essays on the Mucusless Diet Healing System*. He released the first critical edition of the *Mucusless Diet* entitled *Prof. Arnold Ehret's Mucusless Diet Healing System: Annotated, Revised, and Edited by Prof. Spira* in 2014. He is the founder of Mucus-free Life LLC and webmaster of www.mucusfreelife.com.

List of Other Publications

Prof. Arnold Ehret's Mucusless Diet Healing System
Annotated, Revised, and Edited by Prof. Spira

After almost 100 years, the *Mucusless Diet Healing System* has been revised and annotated for twenty-first-century audiences!

*This is a must-read for all
people interested in the Mucusless Diet!*

Find it at www.mucusfreelife.com/revised-mucusless-diet/

Spira Speaks: Dialogs and Essays on the

Mucusless Diet Healing System

Join Prof. Spira for an unprecedented look into the healing power of a mucus-free lifestyle! After losing 110 pounds and overcoming numerous physical ailments, Spira learned that he had a gift for articulating the principles of the diet through writing and music. As he began to interact with health-seekers on the internet in 2005, he realized that written dialogs about the diet could benefit far more than just their intended readers. This book is a compilation of the best writings by Professor Spira on the subject.

What is the *Mucusless Diet Healing System*? How has it helped numerous people overcome illnesses thought to be permanent? What does it take to practice a mucus-free lifestyle in the twenty-first century? Why is the transition diet one of the most misunderstood aspects of the mucusless diet? Spira answers these questions and much more in his unprecedented book that contains never-before released writings about the mucusless diet.

Prof. Arnold Ehret's Rational Fasting for Physical, Mental, and Spiritual Rejuvenation: Introduced and Edited by Prof. Spira

Discover one of Ehret's most vital and influential works, the companion of the Mucusless Diet Healing System. Introducing *Rational Fasting for Physical, Mental, and Spiritual Rejuvenation: Introduced and Edited by Prof. Spira*, now available from Breathair Publishing.

In this masterpiece, Ehret explains how to successfully, safely, and rationally conduct a fast in order to eliminate harmful waste from the body and promote internal healing. Also included are famous essays on Ehret's teachings by Fred Hirsch and long-time devotee Teresa Mitchell.

You will learn:

The Common Fundamental Cause in the Nature of Diseases

Complete Instructions for Fasting

Building a Perfect Body through Fasting

Important Rules for the Faster

How Long to Fast

Why to Fast

When and How to Fast

How Teresa Mitchell Transformed Her Life through Fasting

And Much More!

Pamphlets on Ehret's Teachings

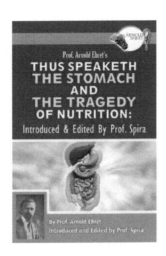 

Thus Speaketh the Stomach and The Tragedy of Nutrition

If your intestines could talk, what would they say? What if you could understand health through the perspective of your stomach? In this unprecedented work, Arnold Ehret gives voice to the stomach and reveals the foundation of human illness.

The Definite Cure of Chronic Constipation and Overcoming Constipation Naturally: Introduction by Prof. Spira

In *The Definite Cure of Chronic Constipation and Overcoming Constipation Naturally*, Prof. Arnold Ehret and his number-one student Fred Hirsch explore the generally constipated condition of the human organism.

The Art of Transition:

Spira's Mucusless Diet Healing System

Menu and Recipe Guide

What does a mucusless diet practitioner actually eat? What kind of transitional mucus-forming foods are best? What are the most effective menu combinations to achieve long-lasting success with the mucusless diet? What are the best transitional cooked and raw menus? What foods and combinations should be avoided at all costs? How can you prepare satisfying mucusless and mucus-lean meals for your family?

These questions and much more will be addressed in Prof. Spira's long-awaited mucusless diet menu and recipe eBook! Stay tuned!

Introduction

Purpose

Popular Fruits, Vegetables, and Vegan Items Omitted from this Book

Organic vs. Non-Organic

Mucus-Lean

    Raw vs. Cooked

    Satisfying Nut and Dried Fruit Combinations

    The Onion Sauté

    Filling Steamed and Baked Vegetable Meals

    Spira's Special "Meat-Away" Meal

Mucusless

　Raw Combination Salads

　Raw Dressings

　Favorite Mono-Fruit Meals

　Favorite Dried Fruits

　Favorite Fruit Combinations

　Vegetable Juices

　Fruit Smoothies and Sauces

　Fresh Fruit Juices

　Sample Combinations and Weekly Menus

Projected Release: Winter 2019

SPIRA'S MUCUSLESS DIET

COACHING & CONSULTATIONS

"After receiving a consultation with Professor Spira, I was able to take my practice of the Mucusless Diet Healing System to a new level. Speaking face to face with an advanced practitioner was key and a true blessing on my journey. I'm looking forward to following up with another in the future!"

—Brian Stern, Certified Bikram Yoga Instructor and Musician

"You truly are amazing. You have done nothing but given all you can to help me and I truly appreciate this. Thank you for 'feeding me.'"

—Samantha Claire, Pianist and Educator

"Spira has experienced the cleansing in a higher level and passes those experiences to us. He teaches us by EXAMPLE and not only by WORDS, which is rare to find in the world we live in."

—Georgia Barretto, Brazilian Jazz Musician

Spira has practiced the mucusless diet and studied the natural hygienic/back-to-nature movements for the past 10 years. During that time, he has advised and helped many in the art of transitioning away from mucus-forming foods. For a limited time, talk with Prof. Spira about your individual needs, challenges, and questions. Skype, telephone, or in-person consultations available! For more information, visit:

www.mucusfreelife.com/diet-coaching

Web Links

Websites

mucusfreelife.com

breathairmusic.com

Facebook

Prof. Spira Fan Page: www.facebook.com/ProfessorSpira

Arnold Ehret Fan Page: www.facebook.com/arnoldehret.us

Arnold Ehret Support Group: www.facebook.com/groups/arnoldehret/

YouTube

Prof. Spira's Breathair-Vision: www.youtube.com/user/professorspira

Twitter

@profspira

@ArnoldEhret1

Visit our Bookstore to Find Books by Arnold Ehret!

www.mucusfreelife.com/storefront/

Spira is now available for mucusless diet consultations/coaching!

www.mucusfreelife.com/storefront/product/mucusless-diet-coaching/

Please Share Your Reviews!

Share your reviews and comments about this book and your experiences with the mucusless diet on Amazon and mucusfreelife.com. Prof. Spira would love to hear how the text has helped you.

PEACE, LOVE, AND BREATH!